HMH |  into Math™

Teacher Edition: Planning and Pacing Guide

Grade 4

Copyright © 2020 by Houghton Mifflin Harcourt Publishing Company

All rights reserved. No part of this work may be reproduced or transmitted in any form or by any means, electronic or mechanical, including photocopying or recording, or by any information storage or retrieval system, without the prior written permission of the copyright owner unless such copying is expressly permitted by federal copyright law. Requests for permission to make copies of any part of the work should be submitted through our Permissions website at https://customercare.hmhco.com/contactus/Permissions. html or mailed to Houghton Mifflin Harcourt Publishing Company, Attn: Intellectual Property Licensing, 9400 Southpark Center Loop, Orlando, Florida 32819-8647.

Common Core State Standards © Copyright 2010. National Governors Association Center for Best Practices and Council of Chief State School Officers. All rights reserved.

This product is not sponsored or endorsed by the Common Core State Standards Initiative of the National Governors Association Center for Best Practices and the Council of Chief State School Officers.

Printed in the U.S.A.

ISBN 978-0-358-11197-9

7 8 9 10   2331   27 26 25 24 23

4500867759   C D E F G

Advocates for Excellence

To develop *Into Math*, we listened to teachers like you, who told us about their unique classroom challenges. Thanks to their voices, *Into Math* is more than just aligned to standards; it was built specifically to help you and your students succeed in the classroom and on high-stakes assessments.

Into Math was developed by a team of esteemed researchers and practitioners. These leaders work tirelessly to evolve instructional practices and advocate for clearer, more holistic, flexible, and active methodology in the classroom.

Edward B. Burger, PhD, is a mathematician who is also the president of Southwestern University in Georgetown, Texas. He is a former Francis Christopher Oakley Third Century Professor of Mathematics at Williams College, and a former vice provost at Baylor University. He has authored or coauthored numerous articles, books, and video series; delivered many addresses and workshops throughout the world; and made many radio and television appearances. He has earned many national honors, including the Robert Foster Cherry Award for Great Teaching. In 2013, he was inducted as one of the first fellows of the American Mathematical Society.

Juli K. Dixon, PhD, is a professor of mathematics education at the University of Central Florida (UCF). She has taught mathematics in urban schools at the elementary, middle, secondary, and post-secondary levels. She is a prolific writer who has published books, textbooks, book chapters, and articles. A sought-after speaker, Dr. Dixon has delivered keynotes and other presentations throughout the United States. Key areas of focus are deepening teachers' content knowledge and communicating and justifying mathematical ideas. She is a past chair of the National Council of Teachers of Mathematics Student Explorations in Mathematics Editorial Panel and a member of the board of directors for the Association of Mathematics Teacher Educators. You can find her on social media at @TheStrokeOfLuck.

Timothy D. Kanold, PhD, is an award-winning international educator, author, and consultant. He is a former superintendent and director of mathematics and science at Adlai E. Stevenson High School District 125 in Lincolnshire, Illinois. He is a past president of the National Council of Supervisors of Mathematics (NCSM) and the Council for the Presidential Awardees of Mathematics (CPAM). He has served on several writing and leadership commissions for National Council of Teachers of Mathematics during the past two decades, including the *Teaching Performance Standards* task force. He presents motivational professional development seminars worldwide with a focus on developing professional learning communities (PLCs) to improve teaching, assessing, and learning of *all* students. He has recently authored nationally recognized articles, books, and textbooks for mathematics education and school leadership, including *What Principals Need to Know About Teaching and Learning Mathematics* and *HEART!: Fully Forming Your Professional Life as a Teacher and Leader.* You can find him on social media at @tkanold.

Matthew R. Larson, PhD, is a past president of the National Council of Teachers of Mathematics (NCTM). Prior to serving as president of NCTM, he was the K–12 mathematics curriculum specialist for Lincoln Public Schools (Nebraska) where he currently serves as associate superintendent for instruction. A prolific speaker and writer, he is the coauthor of more than a dozen professional books. He was a member of the writing teams for the major publications *Principles to Actions: Ensuring Mathematical Success for All* (2014) and *Catalyzing Change in High School Mathematics: Initiating Critical Conversations* (2018). Key areas of focus include access and equity and effective stakeholder communication. He has taught mathematics at the secondary and college levels and held an appointment as an honorary visiting associate professor at Teachers College, Columbia University. You can find him on social media at @mlarson_math.

Steven J. Leinwand is a principal research analyst at the American Institutes for Research (AIR) in Washington, DC, and has nearly 40 years in leadership positions in mathematics education. He is a past president of the National Council of Supervisors of Mathematics and served on the National Council of Teachers of Mathematics Board of Directors. He is the author of numerous articles, books, and textbooks and has made countless presentations with topics including student achievement, reasoning, effective assessment, and successful implementation of standards. You can find him on social media at @steve_leinwand.

Jennifer Lempp is an author and educational consultant. She also currently serves as a coordinator in Fairfax County Public Schools, Virginia. She has taught at the elementary and middle school levels and served as a math coach for many years. She is Nationally Board Certified in Early Adolescence Mathematics and has facilitated professional development at the local, state, and national level on math workshop as a model for differentiated mathematics instruction. You can find her on social media at @Lempp5.

Program Consultants

English Language Development Consultant

Harold Asturias is the director for the Center for Mathematics Excellence and Equity at the Lawrence Hall of Science, University of California. He specializes in connecting mathematics and English language development as well as equity in mathematics education.

Program Consultant

David Dockterman, EdD, operates at the intersection of research and practice. A member of the faculty at the Harvard Graduate School of Education, he provides expertise in curriculum development, adaptive learning, professional development, and growth mindset.

Blended Learning Consultant

Weston Kieschnick, Associate Partner ICLE, a former teacher, principal, instructional development coordinator, and dean of education, Weston Kieschnick has driven change and improved student learning in multiple capacities throughout his educational career. Now, as an experienced instructional coach and associate partner with ICLE, Kieschnick shares his expertise with teachers to transform learning through online and blended models.

STEM Consultants

Michael Despezio has authored many HMH instructional programs for science and mathematics. He has also authored numerous trade books and multimedia programs on various topics and hosted dozens of studio and location broadcasts for various organizations in the US and worldwide. Recently, he has been working with educators to provide strategies for implementing the Next Generation Science Standards.

Bernadine Okoro is a chemical engineer by training and a playwright, novelist, director, and actress by nature. Okoro went from working with patents and biotechnology to teaching in K–12 classrooms. She is a 12-year science educator, Albert Einstein Distinguished Fellow, original author of NGSS and a member of the Diversity and Equity Team. Okoro currently works as a STEM learning advocate and consultant.

Marjorie Frank An educator and linguist by training, a writer and poet by nature, Marjorie Frank has authored and designed a generation of instructional materials in all subject areas. Her other credits include authoring science issues of an award-winning children's magazine, writing game-based digital assessments, developing blended learning materials, and serving as instructional designer and coauthor of school-to-work software. She has also served on the adjunct faculty of Hunter, Manhattan, and Brooklyn Colleges.

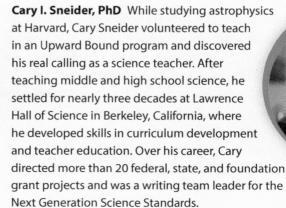

Cary I. Sneider, PhD While studying astrophysics at Harvard, Cary Sneider volunteered to teach in an Upward Bound program and discovered his real calling as a science teacher. After teaching middle and high school science, he settled for nearly three decades at Lawrence Hall of Science in Berkeley, California, where he developed skills in curriculum development and teacher education. Over his career, Cary directed more than 20 federal, state, and foundation grant projects and was a writing team leader for the Next Generation Science Standards.

Math Solutions & Classroom Advisors

Math Solutions Program Consultants

Math Solutions
FOUNDED BY MARILYN BURNS

Deepa Bharath, MEd
Professional Learning Specialist
Math Solutions
Jupiter, Florida

Nicole Bridge, MEd
Professional Learning Specialist
Math Solutions
Attleboro, Massachusetts

Treve Brinkman
Director of Professional Learning
Math Solutions
Denver, Colorado

Lisa K. Bush, MEd
Sr. Director, Professional Development
Math Solutions
Glendale, Arizona

Carol Di Biase
Professional Learning Specialist
Math Solutions
Melbourne, Florida

Stephanie J. Elizondo, MEd
Professional Learning Specialist
Math Solutions
Ocala, Florida

Christine Esch, MEd
Professional Learning Specialist
Math Solutions
Phoenix, Arizona

Le'Vada Gray, MEd
Director of Professional Learning
Math Solutions
Country Club Hills, Illinois

Connie J. Horgan, MEd
Professional Learning Specialist
Math Solutions
Jerome, Idaho

Monica H. Kendall, EdD
Professional Learning Specialist
Math Solutions
Houston, Texas

Lori Ramsey, MEd
Professional Learning Specialist
Math Solutions
Justin, Texas

Lisa Rogers
Professional Learning Specialist
Math Solutions
Cape Coral, Florida

Derek Staves, EdD
Professional Learning Specialist
Math Solutions
Greeley, Colorado

Sheila Yates, MEd
Professional Learning Specialist
Math Solutions
Sioux Falls, South Dakota

Classroom Advisors

Abbey Len Bobbett
Laguna Elementary School
Scottsdale Unified School District
Scottsdale, Arizona

Rebecca Boden
Grant County Board of Education
Grant County Schools
Williamstown, Kentucky

Nicole Bunger
Centennial Elementary
Higley Unified School District
Gilbert, Arizona

Marsha Campbell
Murray Elementary
Hobbs Municipal Schools
Hobbs, New Mexico

Nichole Gard
Palmyra Elementary
Palmyra R-1 School District
Palmyra, Missouri

Dena Morosin
Shasta Elementary School
Klamath County School District
Klamath Falls, Oregon

Joanna O'Brien
Palmyra Elementary
Palmyra R-1 School District
Palmyra, Missouri

Nora Rowe
Peoria Traditional Elementary
Peoria Unified School District
Peoria, Arizona

Terri Trebilcock
Fairmount Elementary
Jefferson County Public Schools
Golden, Colorado

Table of Contents

Table of Contents

Welcome to

Perseverance Powers Student Growth

Designed from the ground up to meet the high expectations of Mathematics Standards, *Into Math* is the only solution built to track, predict, and propel growth for all your students in kindergarten through grade 12.

The Outcomes You Want

The *Into Math* system produces measurable outcomes:

- **students** who have mastered rigorous standards, equipped with skills to persevere when presented with challenging, real-world problems

- **teachers** who grow as professionals, able to apply current research-based strategies and best practices

- **educators** who leverage data to differentiate and adapt, ensuring success in high-stakes assessments

- **families** that use accessible tools to support learning at home

What Makes *Into Math* Students *Unstoppable*?

The *Into Math* system maximizes student growth by helping teachers deliver high-quality instruction while monitoring every student's success.

Focused and Purposeful

Carefully crafted mathematical tasks, differentiated resources, and clear instructional support help teachers put every student front and center. **See pp. PG10–PG23.**

Content Architecture

GROWTH

Teacher Support

Assessments, Data, and Reports

Ongoing and Relevant

Embedded support, classroom videos, resource libraries, and coaching provide learning opportunities for teachers of all levels. **See pp. PG32–PG42.**

Integrated and Actionable

Autoscored assignments and assessments help educators make informed instructional decisions. **See pp. PG24–PG31.**

Content Architecture

Focus, Coherence, and Rigor

In *Into Math*, the progression of topics forms coherent learning arcs. The learning arcs are designed to build a foundation of conceptual understanding before teaching procedures. Opportunities for application occur throughout. An emphasis is placed on connections between concepts and skills. The learning arcs ensure delivery of rigorous instruction.

Learning Arc

Application Throughout

CONCEPTUAL	CONCEPTUAL AND PROCEDURAL	PROCEDURAL
Build Understanding	Connect Concepts and Skills	Apply and Practice

To help you visualize the arc and teach with purpose, *Into Math* has three types of lessons, each with a different focus and containing certain learning task types:

Build Understanding

Conceptual These lessons focus on opportunities for students to make sense of the mathematics and build conceptual understanding with real-world context.

- Spark Your Learning
- Build Understanding

Connect Concepts and Skills

Bridging These lessons focus on having students connect different conceptual representations, approaches, or strategies to more efficient procedures.

- Spark Your Learning
- Build Understanding
- Step It Out

Apply and Practice

Procedural These lessons focus on opportunities for students to develop procedural fluency and to apply concepts and procedures.

- Step It Out

Learning Tasks

Spark Your Learning tasks promote conceptual understanding. During these low floor/high ceiling tasks, students leverage prior learning and select manipulatives or representations that serve as their entry point. Teachers provide just-in-time support, helping students engage in meaningful discourse and learn to persevere. Teachers lead the class to shared understanding in a student-centered environment.

Build Understanding tasks are learning opportunities designed to help students understand lesson concepts. Teachers take a more active role, guiding discussion during whole-class instruction.

Step It Out tasks build upon students' conceptual understanding to promote procedural understanding and fluency. Teachers help students understand why the procedures are efficient and how they can be applied to solve similar problem types.

Creating a Learning Arc

Juli K. Dixon, Ph.D.
Professor, Mathematics Education
University of Central Florida
Orlando, Florida

Teaching with Coherence

For students to make the most of their mathematics education, topics should be taught with coherence. This means that topics should be taught as connected ideas rather than within individual silos. Consider multi-digit multiplication. Linking the area model with the partial products algorithm provides a visual representation for this important topic (see Figure 1) and sets the stage for finding areas of rectangles and combined rectangles.

A benefit of making connections within different mathematical topics is that students have multiple pathways to retrieve what they learned and therefore rely less on rote memorization. For example, students can make sense of multi-digit multiplication by recalling their work with area and linking it to partial products.

Connecting Concepts and Procedures

Rigor describes the important balance between concepts and procedures. While balance is important, so is the order with which concepts and procedures are addressed. Concepts must be taught before procedures; otherwise, there is no motivation to make sense of the mathematics prior to using more efficient processes.

Figure 1 from Grade 4, Lesson 8.3

Step It Out

2 In the storage closet, there are 17 different types of paint brushes with 23 of each type. How many paint brushes are there?

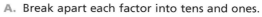

A. Break apart each factor into tens and ones.

$17 = \underline{10} + \underline{7}$

$23 = \underline{20} + \underline{3}$

B. Label the area model with the factors.

C. Use the Distributive Property to find the partial products.

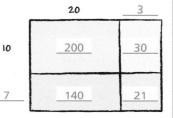

$(10 \times 20) + (\underline{10} \times \underline{3}) + (\underline{7} \times \underline{20}) + (\underline{7} \times \underline{3})$

  10 × 2 tens   10 × 3 ones   7 × 2 tens   7 × 3 ones

D. Add the partial products to find the whole product.

$\boxed{200} + \boxed{30} + \boxed{140} + \boxed{21} = \underline{391}$

E. There are ___391___ paint brushes in the storage closet.

Consider adding fractions with unlike denominators in Grade 5, Module 6. If students are taught the procedure to

- find a common denominator,
- create equivalent fractions using that denominator, and
- add the numerators of the equivalent fractions

prior to understanding why that's necessary, then students may make the error of adding both the numerators and the denominators if they confuse the rules. In contrast, if students make sense of describing fractions with the same-sized pieces in order to combine them prior to learning the standard algorithm for adding fractions, the students are less likely to make errors with the procedures because they understand the reasoning behind the process. The learning arc is complete when concepts are taught first and then those concepts are linked to more efficient processes before the procedures are practiced and applied.

Content Architecture

Lesson Design

***Into Math* classrooms are different.** Lessons are designed to help you incorporate research-based best practices into your instruction. This design is found in the print student books and in the interactive digital lessons, enabling you to utilize either pathway or a blended approach.

SPARK YOUR LEARNING

5-10 minutes

Teachers guide student discussions, help students persevere as they work together on a mathematical task, and build shared understanding by selecting students to explain their reasoning.

LEARN TOGETHER

5-10 minutes per task

Teachers facilitate learning during whole-group instruction, which ensures that students continue to play an active role in sharing their reasoning and understanding. In *Step It Out* features, students connect important processes and procedures to mathematical concepts.

CHECK UNDERSTANDING

5 minutes

Teachers utilize this quick formative assessment to determine whether students have mastered lesson content and to identify which differentiation resources will be most useful for each student.

The pacing recommendations within each lesson can be modified based on individual preferences and teaching styles. Yearlong pacing recommendations are provided in the Pacing Guide starting on PG46.

DIFFERENTIATION OPTIONS

Fill remaining time

A variety of leveled resources are available to help teachers differentiate early and effectively.

WRAP-UP AND HOMEWORK

5 minutes

Teachers bring the class together to summarize, using Exit Tickets, journal writing, "I Can" self-assessment, or anchor charts.

Small Groups

Teachers use the Tabletop Flipchart activity to guide small groups of students.

Independent Practice

Students can continue to the *On Your Own* portion of the lesson.

Math Centers

Print and digital games, readers, and activities can be used to set up centers.

Waggle

Waggle complements *Into Math* with personalized learning that supports students at all proficiency levels.

Content Architecture

Promoting Conceptual Understanding

Not All Tasks Are Equal. The *Spark Your Learning* tasks have been carefully crafted to promote reasoning and problem solving. The tasks can be solved using various solution strategies and have a low floor and a high ceiling to ensure every student can make progress and build understanding.

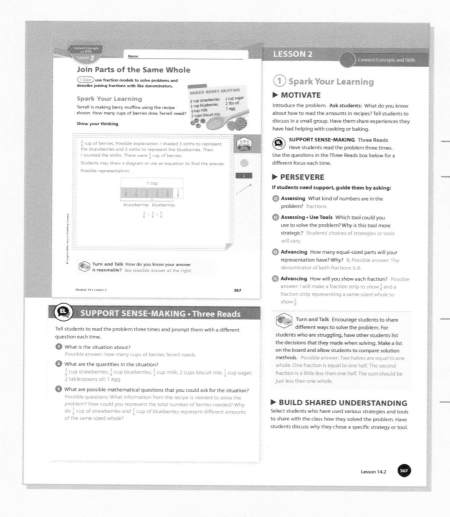

Teachers begin a **Spark Your Learning** task by setting goals and using language-development routines to help students understand the task, if needed.

Teachers support **productive perseverance** and foster a growth mindset as students work through the task. The Teacher Edition includes **student work samples** and provides support to help teachers correct common errors and assess and advance student understanding.

The **Talk Moves** routines encourage student discourse and also help teachers elicit reasoning and guide students.

A *Spark Your Learning* task is complete when the class comes to shared understanding and the teacher celebrates **student success**.

See It in Action
Professional Learning support includes classroom videos with hints, tips, and commentary from experts and authors.

Promoting Perseverance

Juli K. Dixon, Ph.D.
Professor, Mathematics Education
University of Central Florida
Orlando, Florida

Rigorous Tasks

There is little argument that students need to learn to persevere. Where the struggle exists is in determining the pathway to this important outcome. It begins with a good task. Good tasks are rigorous. Providing rigorous tasks sets the stage for students to engage in worthwhile activity around learning mathematics. Good tasks have "low floors" and "high ceilings" so that students have access to the content regardless of their prior achievement.

A rigorous task is one that supports students to do the sense-making. A goal might be to make connections between concepts and procedures, or possibly to determine a solution process when a procedure for the solution has not yet been introduced. Students are expected to explain and justify their thinking. Rigorous tasks afford students the opportunities to develop productive habits of mind around mathematical problem solving.

Just-in-Time Scaffolding

All too often, with best intentions, teachers or resources undermine the value of a good task by providing scaffolding too early. It is tempting to provide scaffolding to students at the first sign of struggle or even in anticipation of student struggle. However, if the struggle is productive, this scaffolding should be withheld. Instead of providing scaffolding just in case students might need it, scaffolding should be offered just in time, when there is evidence that a student's struggle is no longer productive.

While the opportunity to develop perseverance is reliant on access to good tasks, it is supported during instruction by effective teaching. For students to develop perseverance, they must engage in productive struggle. This means that scaffolding, on the student page or from the teacher, needs to be managed in a way that supports students to do the sense-making.

Scaffolding should be provided when students' engagement with the task is no longer productive or when the students' work is not leading to the learning objective. A key to effective teaching is to know when to provide the scaffolding and when to step aside to allow students to persevere.

Content Architecture

Real-World Relevance

Is your weight on the Moon proportional to your weight on Earth? Am I on track to meet my goal for number of steps walked today? How did people 10,000 years ago incorporate geometric designs into their jewelry? Projects and tasks in *Into Math* are carefully crafted, not only to ensure they have the appropriate level of rigor, but also to ensure students remain engaged and see the relevance of math in the world around them.

Each unit opens with a career-related project that students can work on throughout the unit.

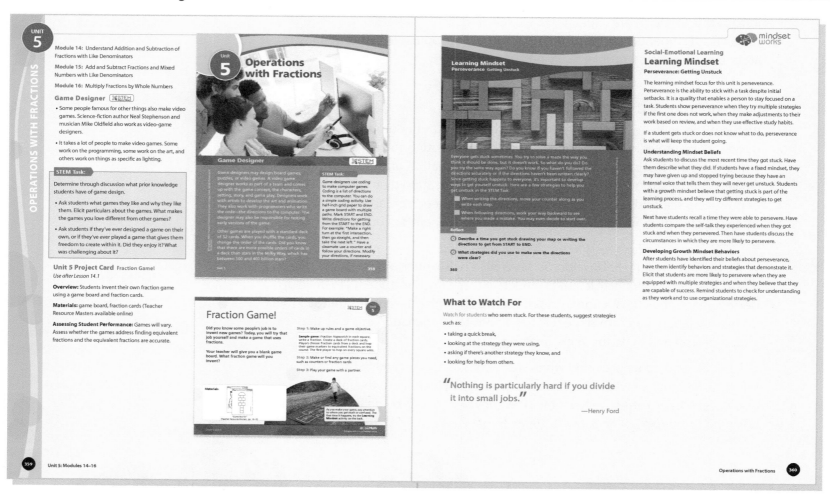

Cross-curricular tasks are found throughout the program, including STEM problems in each module and STEM-themed unit projects.

Opportunities, strategies, and support to help students focus on mindset are embedded in every lesson and in the unit-level projects.

Mathematical Practices and Processes

Into Math provides a focus on Mathematical Practices and Processes aligned to the lesson's learning goal and the tasks that meet the learning goal.

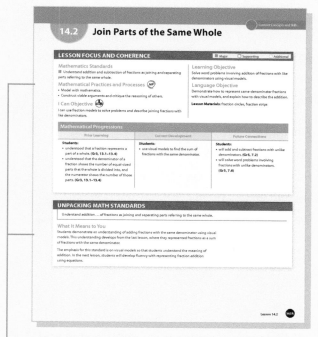

Each lesson focuses on Mathematical Practices and Processes based on the lesson's learning goal.

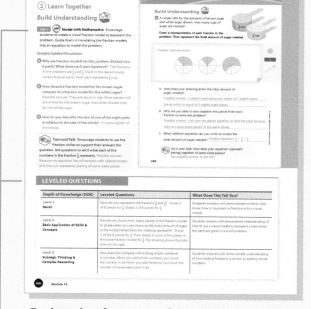

Each task references a focused Mathematical Practice and Process and includes probing questions to support student engagement and depth of understanding.

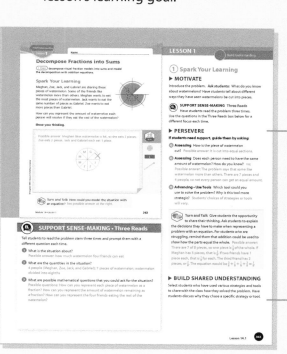

Students choose strategies and tools. The Teacher Edition provides additional support with Use Tools questions.

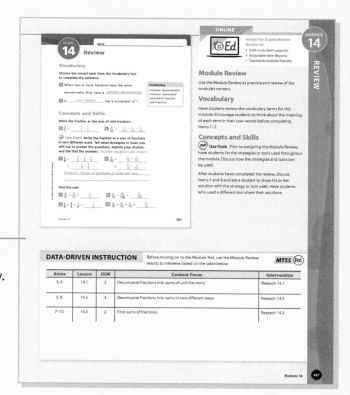

Students solidify their understanding and choose tools strategically. The Teacher Edition provides additional recommendations for student discourse.

Content Architecture

Mathematical Practices and Processes	Questions to Ask:
Make sense of problems and persevere in solving them. • *Spark Your Learning* tasks provide low floor/high ceiling, real-world problems accessible to all students. Students make sense of these problems to plan their solution pathways. • *Build Understanding* tasks present problems situations with some scaffolding, which supports students while they are making sense of problems. • *Turn and Talk* questions foster collaboration by asking students to discuss their solution pathways or to discuss how they know their solution makes sense.	• What is the problem asking? • How will you use that information? • What other information do you need? • What is another way to solve that problem? • What can you do if you don't know how to solve a problem? • Have you solved a problem similar to this one? • How do you know your answer makes sense?
Reason abstractly and quantitatively. • *Spark Your Learning* tasks provide real-world problems, accessible to all students. Each task is often supported with the language routine *Three Reads* to help students' use of abstract reasoning and consideration of quantities and units. • *Build Understanding* and *Step It Out* tasks present problems that require quantitative reasoning. • *Turn and Talk* questions ask students to discuss the representation of the problem and the meaning of the quantities and units within the context of the problem and solution. • *On Your Own* and *More Practice/Homework* include practice problems labeled *Reason*.	• What quantities are referenced? • How are the quantities related? • How can you represent this situation? • How are the quantities and the units related? • What are the correct units for the quantities in the problem? • How do you know your answer is reasonable?
Construct viable arguments and critique the reasoning of others. • *Connect to Vocabulary* provides context and definitions for academic vocabulary. • The language routine *Critique, Correct, and Clarify* has students correct work having a flawed explanation, argument, or solution method. • *Build Understanding* tasks encourage students to describe or explain their reasoning. • *Turn and Talk* questions ask students to discuss a flawed explanation, argument, or solution method. • *On Your Own* and *More Practice/Homework* include practice problems labeled *Construct Arguments* and *Critique Reasoning*.	• Will that method always work? How do you know? • What do you think about what the other student said? • Who agrees or disagrees, and why? • Does anyone have another way of looking at that? • What do you think will happen if…? • When would that not be true? • Does that make sense to you? Why?
Model with mathematics. • *Spark Your Learning* tasks provide students with opportunities to use mathematics they know to represent and solve a problem. • *Build Understanding* and *Step It Out* tasks present problems and then have students decide how to model the problems with mathematics. • *Turn and Talk* questions ask students to describe or explain their models and why they chose a specific mathematical representation. • *On Your Own* and *More Practice/Homework* include practice problems labeled *Model with Mathematics*.	• Why is that a good model for this problem? • How can you use a simpler problem to help you find the answer? • What conclusions can you make from your model? • Do your results make sense within the context of the problem? • How would you change your model if…?

Mathematical Practices and Processes	Questions to Ask:
Use appropriate tools strategically. • *Unit Openers* include a STEM task that has students use mathematics they know to complete a task and then reflect on strategies and tools they used. • *Spark Your Learning* tasks prompt students to choose tools as part of their solution pathways. Students are asked to explain their choices. • *Build Understanding* and *Step It Out* tasks have students choose tools and describe or explain their choices. • *Module Review* provides an opportunity for students to review the module content and state the strategy and tool they used to solve a problem. • *Turn and Talk* questions ask students to describe or explain why they chose a specific tool. • *On Your Own* and *More Practice/Homework* include practice problems labeled *Use Tools*.	• What could you use to help you solve the problem? • What strategy could you use to make that calculation easier? • How would estimation help you solve that problem? • Why did you decide to use…?
Attend to precision. • *Build Understanding* and *Step It Out* tasks provide vocabulary once students have explored the concept at point of learning and often are paired with *Connect to Vocabulary*. • The *Interactive Glossary* provides opportunities for students to make sense of vocabulary by having students record in their own words or with examples. • *Step It Out* tasks, *On Your Own,* and *More Practice/Homework* provide opportunities for students to focus on performing calculations accurately and efficiently. • *Turn and Talk* questions provide opportunities for students to communicate precisely to others by using accurate mathematical terms and definitions. • *On Your Own* and *More Practice/Homework* include practice problems labeled *Attend to Precision*.	• How do you know your answer is reasonable? • How can you use mathematics vocabulary in your explanation? • How do you know those answers are equivalent? • What does that mean?
Look for and make use of structure. • *Spark Your Learning* tasks provide opportunities for students to relate to structures they know as a way to make sense of the problem and find a solution pathway. • *Build Understanding* and *Step It Out* tasks connect concepts by showing an example and asking students to explain or describe a structure based on what is shown in the example. • *Turn and Talk* questions ask students to identify, describe, or explain a structure they used to solve a problem. • *On Your Own* and *More Practice/Homework* include practice problems labeled *Use Structure*.	• What rule did you use to make. . . ? • Why can you use that property in this problem? • How is that like…?
Look for and express regularity in repeated reasoning. • *Spark Your Learning* tasks provide opportunities for students to notice repeated calculations and other patterns leading to a general method or shortcut. • *Build Understanding* and *Step It Out* tasks connect repeated reasoning to a new general method or shortcut. • *Turn and Talk* questions ask students to describe or explain their reasoning. • *On Your Own* and *More Practice/Homework* include practice problems labeled *Use Repeated Reasoning*.	• How did you discover that pattern? • What other patterns can you find? • What do you remember about…? • What happens when…? • What if you…instead of…? • What might be a shortcut for…?

Content Architecture

Language Development

Language development and the development of mathematical understanding are interdependent. All students must be able to listen, speak, read, write, and converse to meet the rigorous expectations of standards and become proficient problem solvers.

B. What does each unit fraction represent in the problem?

_____

C. What addition equation can you write to model the weight of hamburger as a sum of the weight of the patties?

_____

D. How many $\frac{1}{6}$-pound hamburger patties do Tony and

his family have? _____

Connect to Vocabulary

A **unit fraction** tells the part of a whole that each piece represents. The numerator of a unit fraction is always 1.

Before teaching new vocabulary, *Into Math* ensures that students have an opportunity to first build a foundation of conceptual understanding. Vocabulary emerges once students have the conceptual foundation on which to build meaning.

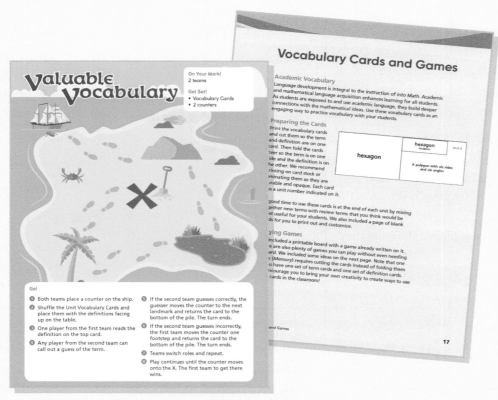

Vocabulary cards can be used with vocabulary games. The eGlossary includes vocabulary terms and definitions translated into ten different languages.

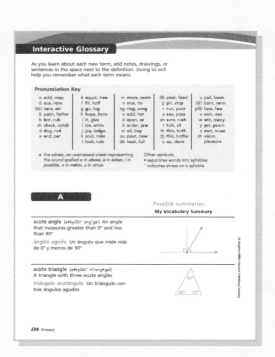

The Interactive Glossary provides space for students to make graphic organizers or drawings for each new vocabulary term.

Harold Asturias
Director, Center for Mathematics
Excellence and Equity
Lawrence Hall of Science
University of California
Berkeley, California

"We must explicitly teach the language of mathematics in order to give students—especially English learners—access to mathematics."

Math is a second language for ALL students. *Into Math* is built on four design principles from the Stanford Center for Assessment, Learning, and Equity (SCALE). These four design principles promote the use and development of language as an integral part of instruction.[1]

1 Support Sense-Making

Scaffold tasks when needed, being sure to amplify (instead of simplify) language for students.

2 Optimize Output

Help students describe their mathematical reasoning and understanding.

3 Cultivate Conversation

Facilitate mathematical conversations among students.

4 Maximize Linguistic and Cognitive Meta-Awareness

Help students evaluate their use of language and see how mathematical ideas, reasoning, and language are connected.

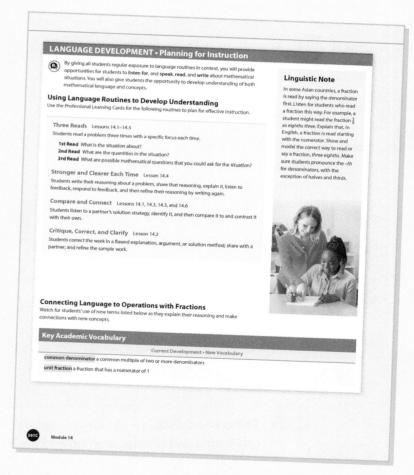

The Language Routines as well as new and review vocabulary words are summarized on the Language Development page at the beginning of each module.

---

1) J. Zwiers, et al., *Principles for the Design of Mathematics Curricula: Promoting Language and Content Development* (Stanford, CA: Stanford University, 2017).

Content Architecture

Language Development

The **5 Routines for Language Development** help teachers promote the design principles during instruction with routines that are structured, but adaptable, in a format for amplifying, assessing, and developing students' language. These Routines provide opportunities for students to listen, speak, and write about mathematical situations with practices that are appropriate and effective for all **language proficiency levels**.

1 **Three Reads** – To ensure understanding of mathematical questions, students read a problem three times with a specific focus each time.

> **(EL) SUPPORT SENSE-MAKING • Three Reads**
>
> Tell students to read the problem stem three times and prompt them with a different question each time.
>
> **1** What is the situation about?
> Possible answer: buying tickets to the play
>
> **2** What are the quantities in the situation?
> 5 tickets; $100 per ticket
>
> **3** What are possible mathematical questions that you could ask for the situation?
> Possible questions: How much does one ticket cost? How much do 2 tickets cost?

2 **Stronger and Clearer Each Time** – Students use structure to write their reasoning behind a problem, share and explain their reasoning, listen to and respond to feedback, and then write again to refine their reasoning.

> **(EL) CULTIVATE CONVERSATIONS**
> **Stronger and Clearer**
>
> Have students share their answers. Emphasize that there is more than one "correct" answer. Encourage students to realize that using 32 longs might be an efficient way to represent the problem. Then have students refine their answers to select their preferred method.

3 **Compare and Connect** – Meta-awareness is strengthened as students listen to a partner's solution strategy and then identify, compare, and contrast this mathematical strategy.

> **(EL) CONNECT MATH IDEAS, REASONING, AND LANGUAGE** Compare and Connect
>
> Have students discuss the similarities and differences between the **Commutative Property of Multiplication** and the Commutative Property of Addition.

4 **Critique, Correct, and Clarify** – Students correct sample work having a flawed explanation, argument, or solution method and share with a partner to reflect on and then refine the sample work..

> **(EL) OPTIMIZE OUTPUT** Critique, Correct, and Clarify
> Point out to students that for **Problems 3 and 4** they will need to determine if the exact answers are reasonable. Encourage students to describe why the answers do or do not make sense and review explanations with a partner. Students should refine their responses after their discussions with a partner.

5 **Collect and Display** – Students capture oral words and phrases learned and build a collective reference containing illustrations connected to mathematical concepts and terms within each module.

> **ANCHOR-CHART OPTION**
>
> As you progress through the module, build and display an anchor chart.
>
> **(EL) CONNECT MATH IDEAS, REASONING, AND LANGUAGE** Collect and Display
>
> Have students build their own anchor chart in their Practice and Homework Journal.
>
> A completed chart for the module is shown here.

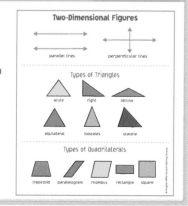

Teacher Tabletop Flipcharts, designed for reteaching and reinforcing each lesson's content with small groups, contain leveled scaffolding and support for English learners. These scaffolding suggestions ensure teachers will maintain the rigor and cognitive complexity level required for mathematical reasoning when supporting English learners.

Three proficiency levels

(EL) Proficiency Level

Beginning

Have students demonstrate their understanding of the fraction models. **Say:** Point to a whole divided into four parts. Have students shade pieces to represent the fractions in the expression $\frac{1}{4} + \frac{2}{4}$. **Ask:** If you add 1 one-fourth piece to 2 one-fourth pieces, how many one-fourth pieces do you have? Have students count on the model and write the fraction.

Intermediate

Have students describe the first set of fraction models using these sentence frames: The whole is divided into _____ parts. Each part is one _____. **Ask:** How many pieces do you shade for $\frac{1}{4}$? For $\frac{2}{4}$? What is the sum?

Advanced

Have students make a fraction model of $\frac{1}{4} + \frac{2}{4}$, find the sum, and explain their work to a partner. Students should use the words *whole, part,* and *sum*.

School Home Letters are available in English, Spanish, Haitian-Creole, and Portuguese.

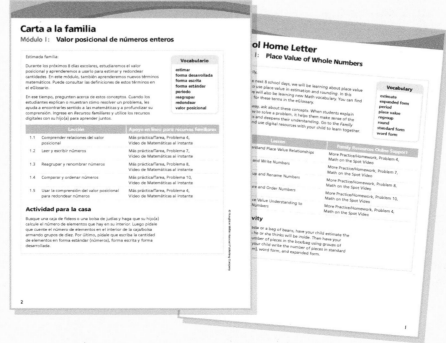

Assessments, Data, and Reports

Assess and Act to Accelerate Every Student

To help students grow, we must first understand where they are and what they need. Assessment tools embedded throughout *Into Math* monitor individual student progress and help teachers understand where students are tracking at any given point. The snapshot below represents what a student's data profile could look like after using *Into Math* for 95 days.

Administered three times per year, this adaptive assessment provides a Quantile® score and is predictive of performance on high-stakes assessment.

These short assessments diagnose prerequisite-skills readiness, inform grouping, and measure progress.

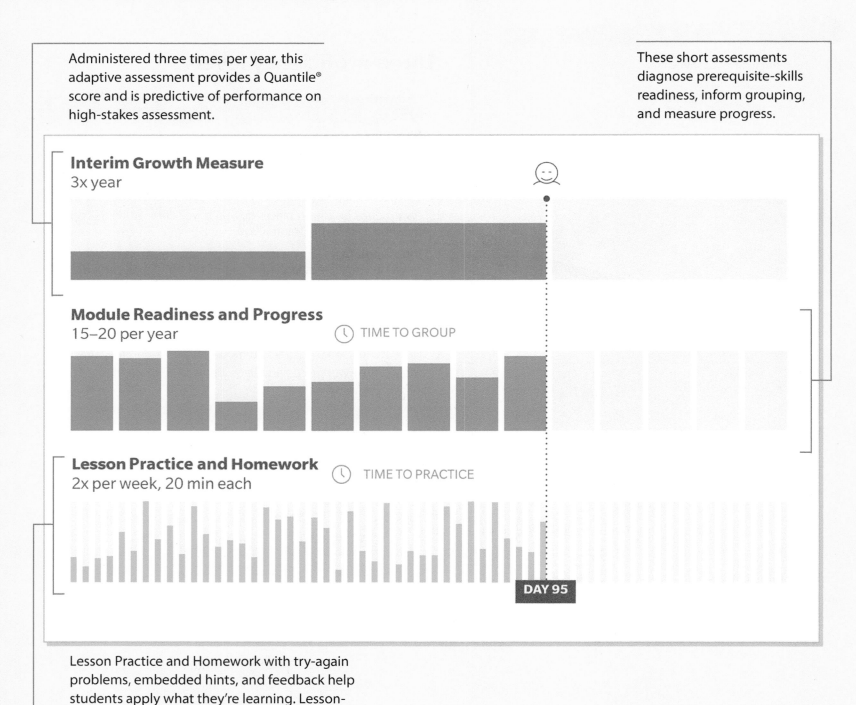

Interim Growth Measure
3x year

Module Readiness and Progress
15–20 per year   TIME TO GROUP

Lesson Practice and Homework
2x per week, 20 min each   TIME TO PRACTICE

DAY 95

Lesson Practice and Homework with try-again problems, embedded hints, and feedback help students apply what they're learning. Lesson-level formative assessments provide data that help teachers differentiate effectively.

Steven J. Leinwand
Principal Research Analyst
American Institutes for Research
Washington, D.C.

Assessment Is Only as Good as How We Use the Data

Assessment as Evidence Gathering

We know that effective assessments are far more than just tests we use to help us grade students. Instead, effective assessments are powerful vehicles for gathering evidence of readiness to learn (diagnostic), for learning (formative), and of learning (summative). We also know that the strength and usefulness of the evidence we gather depends on the alignment of these assessments with our standards and our learning goals, as well as on the balance among skills, concepts, and applications; and among levels of depth of knowledge found in our assessments.

We plan, and we teach. That is, we focus most on our curriculum and our instruction. However, the glue that holds much of our work together and that answers the critical questions about how successful we are being with our planning and teaching is our system of assessments.

Making Effective Use of the Evidence We Collect

Consider the questions to which we all seek reliable answers:

- Are my students ready for the material I'm about to teach?
- Is what I hoped to convey understood by my students? How well? What appears to need more reinforcement?
- Have my instructional strategies worked, or do they need adjustment?
- Can my students apply what they have learned?
- Have my students made connections with previously learned skills and concepts?
- Do I have to reteach the material?
- Which students need additional attention?
- What specific interventions are needed?
- Has previously taught material been retained?

We use diagnostic, formative, and summative assessments to gather data that help us answer each of these questions, but it is how these data are used that makes all the difference. For example, teachers regularly adjust their lesson plans and teach prerequisite skills and concepts on the basis of diagnostic assessments. Similarly, teachers celebrate success, group students, and reteach content based on formative assessments. Far too infrequently, teachers use summative assessments to identify class and individual problems and gaps, reteach in different ways, and incorporate additional instruction into upcoming units. Finally, teachers use all of these data to revise teaching activities and pacing.

Ed: Your Friend in Learning

Teachers are the key to ensuring student growth. That's why we've designed *Into Math* with teachers' needs front of mind. Ed: Your Friend in Learning is your new friend in teaching, designed specifically to help you regain time and easily plan, create, and implement high-impact instruction from one simple platform.

Within *Into Math*, data collection is automated; differentiation is targeted, clear, and easy to use; and professional development is embedded. The experience is both intuitive and customizable for teachers, allowing for simplicity in all areas of instruction.

Interim Growth Measure

This powerful growth-measure assessment is designed to be administered in 40 minutes three times per year. The system utilizes a secure bank of assessments to adapt to each student's ability and maps progress on the Quantile Framework®.

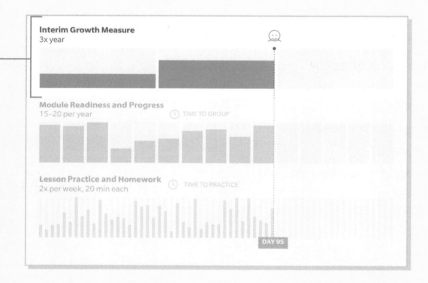

Students can skip questions if needed and access read-aloud support. Feedback that encourages perseverance helps to motivate students.

Dynamic Reporting

Teachers can drill down into data for deeper insights into student performance. Multiple reports and views enable teachers to select those that work best for them, including charts, detailed comparisons, and totals.

Assignment reports show detailed results for each assignment, including an item analysis view.

Standards reports show progress toward mastery of each of the Mathematics Standards.

Quantile® Measure	Tested Proficiency	Growth From Previous Test	State Forecasted Proficiency
1006Q	● Proficient	↗ 116Q	Level 3 (Proficient)
890Q	● Proficient	↗ 41Q	Level 3 (Proficient)
849Q	● Basic	N/A	Level 2 (Basic)

Growth Reports help identify intervention needs and are linked to recommendations and groupings.

Assessments, Data, and Reports

Module Readiness and Progress

Whether you use the autoscored digital assessments or the paper-and-pencil versions in the Assessment Guide, the module assessments make it easy for teachers to leverage data. A variety of reports available on Ed: Your Friend in Learning give you unparalleled insight into student performance.

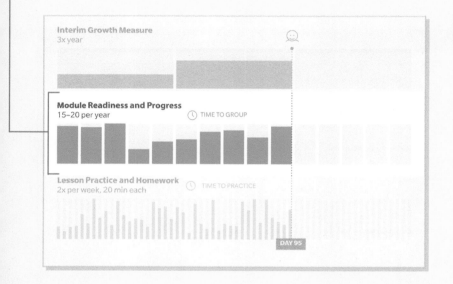

The Module Review in the Student Edition helps prepare students for the Module Test. The Module Test is a summative assessment for monitoring student progress. Intervention recommendations are provided for students who need extra support.

The module *Are You Ready?* is a diagnostic assessment of important prerequisite skills for the upcoming module. A Data-Driven Intervention chart is available in the Teacher Edition.

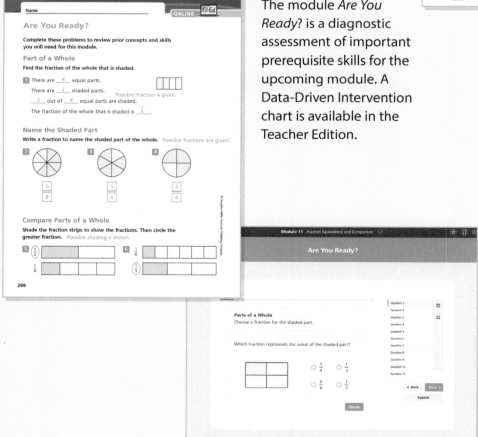

Data-Driven Grouping

One of the most valuable and time-saving tools for teachers is the online Recommend Groups feature. It synthesizes data from assessments and places students into leveled groups. You can easily modify the recommended groups yourself as needed.

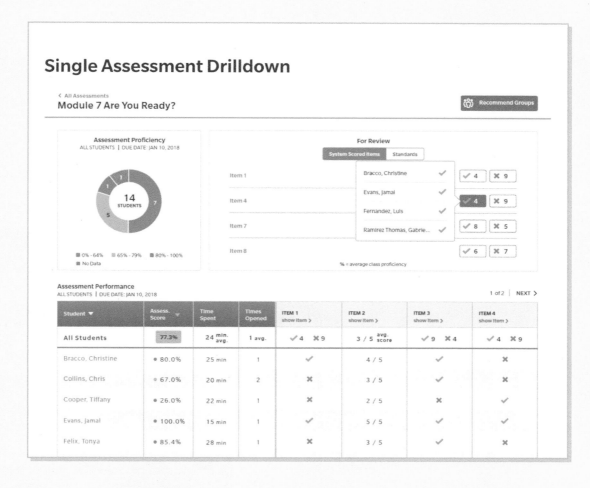

From your groups, assign differentiated resources based on student performance.

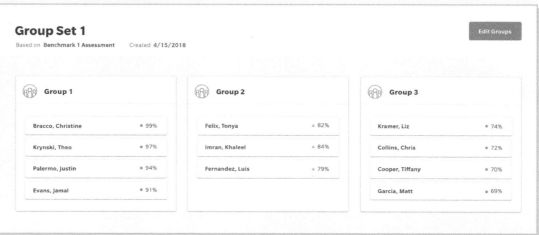

Assessments, Data, and Reports

Lesson Practice and Homework

MAKING SURE EVERY STUDENT GROWS Lesson-level formative assessments and the *Into Math* system reports help teachers differentiate, ensuring every student feels appropriately challenged and makes progress toward lesson goals.

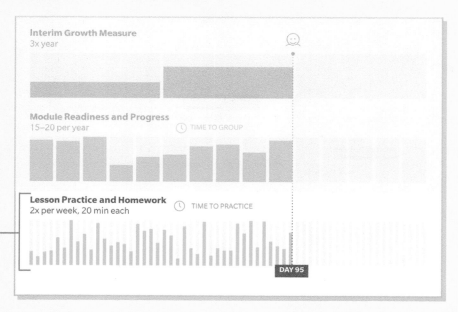

TEACHER EDITION The Teacher Edition shows the variety of differentiated resources available for each lesson.

FLIPCHART Teachers can work with students who have not yet mastered lesson content in small groups using the Tabletop Flipchart Mini-Lesson. It provides an alternative approach to help students who are *Almost There* master lesson content. Small-group activities for students who are *On Track* or *Ready for More* are printed in the Teacher Edition.

MATH CENTER KIT
The differentiated centers kit contains additional resources for use in math centers. These resources include games, readers, standards practice, fluency builders, and projects.

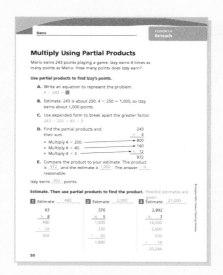

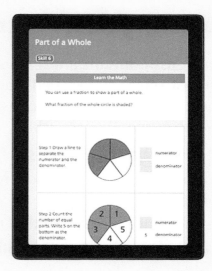

LEVERAGE THE POWER OF STUDENT DATA

Interactive versions of Reteach, Challenge, Additional Practice, Fluency, RtI Tier 2, and RtI Tier 3 worksheets can be assigned online, and teachers can see student results in reports.

Reteach Worksheet

Interactive RtI Tier 3

EMPOWER STUDENTS WITH *WAGGLE*™

Waggle can supplement your *Into Math* instruction by providing adaptive, targeted student practice.

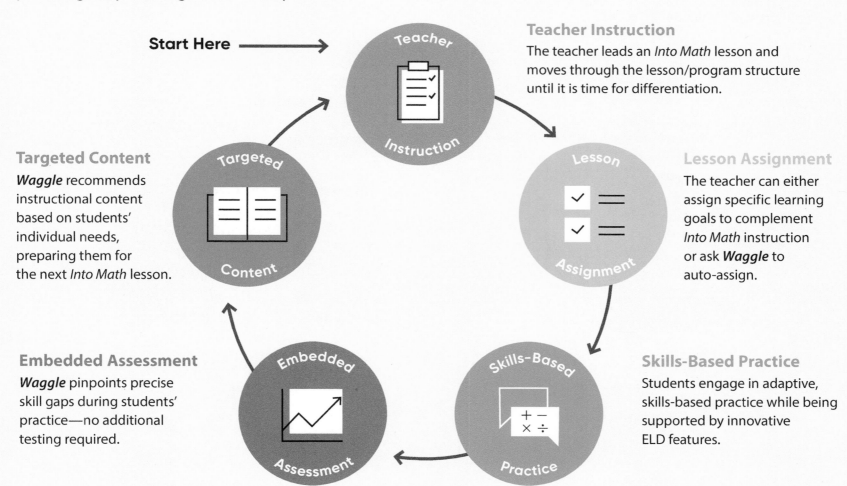

Start Here

Teacher Instruction
The teacher leads an *Into Math* lesson and moves through the lesson/program structure until it is time for differentiation.

Targeted Content
Waggle recommends instructional content based on students' individual needs, preparing them for the next *Into Math* lesson.

Lesson Assignment
The teacher can either assign specific learning goals to complement *Into Math* instruction or ask *Waggle* to auto-assign.

Embedded Assessment
Waggle pinpoints precise skill gaps during students' practice—no additional testing required.

Skills-Based Practice
Students engage in adaptive, skills-based practice while being supported by innovative ELD features.

Supporting Best Practices

Into Math classrooms maximize student growth by providing teachers with content designed around research-based, effective teaching practices, such as those described in *Principles to Actions* (NCTM, 2014).[1]

- Establish mathematics goals to focus learning.
- Implement tasks that promote reasoning and problem solving.
- Use and connect mathematical representations.
- Facilitate meaningful mathematical discourse.
- Pose purposeful questions.
- Build procedural fluency from conceptual understanding.
- Support productive struggle in learning mathematics.
- Elicit and use evidence of student thinking.

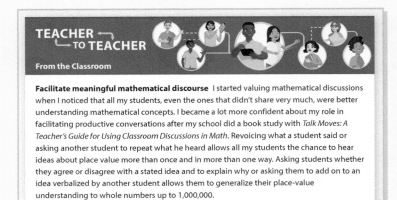

TEACHER TO TEACHER

From the Classroom

Facilitate meaningful mathematical discourse I started valuing mathematical discussions when I noticed that all my students, even the ones that didn't share very much, were better understanding mathematical concepts. I became a lot more confident about my role in facilitating productive conversations after my school did a book study with *Talk Moves: A Teacher's Guide for Using Classroom Discussions in Math*. Revoicing what a student said or asking another student to repeat what he heard allows all my students the chance to hear ideas about place value more than once and in more than one way. Asking students whether they agree or disagree with a stated idea and to explain why or asking them to add on to an idea verbalized by another student allows them to generalize their place-value understanding to whole numbers up to 1,000,000.

Teacher to Teacher tips, aligned to the NCTM Effective Mathematics Teaching Practices, were written by educators for educators.

___

1) National Council of Teachers of Mathematics, *Principles to Actions: Ensuring Mathematical Success for All* (Reston, VA: NCTM, 2014).

Student work samples help teachers understand student thinking behind possible solution pathways.

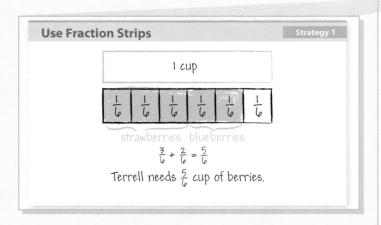

Use Fraction Strips — Strategy 1

1 cup

$$\frac{1}{6} \quad \frac{1}{6} \quad \frac{1}{6} \quad \frac{1}{6} \quad \frac{1}{6} \quad \frac{1}{6}$$

strawberries   blueberries

$$\frac{3}{6} + \frac{2}{6} = \frac{5}{6}$$

Terrell needs $\frac{5}{6}$ cup of berries.

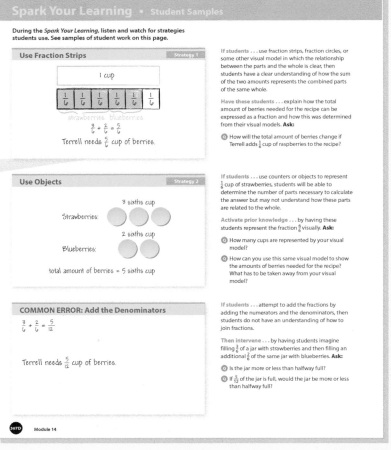

Spark Your Learning • Student Samples

During the *Spark Your Learning*, listen and watch for strategies students use. See samples of student work on this page.

Use Fraction Strips — Strategy 1

1 cup

$$\frac{1}{6} \quad \frac{1}{6} \quad \frac{1}{6} \quad \frac{1}{6} \quad \frac{1}{6} \quad \frac{1}{6}$$

strawberries   blueberries

$$\frac{3}{6} + \frac{2}{6} = \frac{5}{6}$$

Terrell needs $\frac{5}{6}$ cup of berries.

If students . . . use fraction strips, fraction circles, or some other visual model in which the relationship between the parts and the whole is clear, then students have a clear understanding of how the sum of the two amounts represents the combined parts of the same whole.

Have these students . . . explain how the total amount of berries needed for the recipe can be expressed as a fraction and how this was determined from their visual models. **Ask:**

How will the total amount of berries change if Terrell adds $\frac{1}{6}$ cup of raspberries to the recipe?

Use Objects — Strategy 2

Strawberries: 3 sixths cup

2 sixths cup
Blueberries:

total amount of berries = 5 sixths cup

If students . . . use counters or objects to represent $\frac{1}{6}$ cup of strawberries, students will be able to determine the number of parts necessary to calculate the answer but may not understand how these parts are related to the whole.

Activate prior knowledge . . . by having these students represent the fraction $\frac{5}{6}$ visually. **Ask:**

How many cups are represented by your visual model?

How can you use this same visual model to show the amounts of berries needed for the recipe? What has to be taken away from your visual model?

COMMON ERROR: Add the Denominators

$$\frac{3}{6} + \frac{2}{6} = \frac{5}{12}$$

Terrell needs $\frac{5}{12}$ cup of berries.

If students . . . attempt to add the fractions by adding the numerators and the denominators, then students do not have an understanding of how to join fractions.

Then intervene . . . by having students imagine filling $\frac{3}{6}$ of a jar with strawberries and then filling an additional $\frac{2}{6}$ of the same jar with blueberries. **Ask:**

Is the jar more or less than halfway full?

If $\frac{5}{12}$ of the jar is full, would the jar be more or less than halfway full?

367D   Module 14

Carefully crafted tasks, student-centered learning, small groups, and hands-on manipulatives play important roles in an *Into Math* classroom. The *Into Math* Teacher Edition contains point-of-use support to help teachers facilitate learning and implement research-based best practices into their instruction.

Every module includes a professional learning video that features a teacher or HMH author working with real students who are engaging with actual content from the program. The videos include modeling and discussion of effective teaching practices and also feature the Language Routines and Talk Moves strategies.

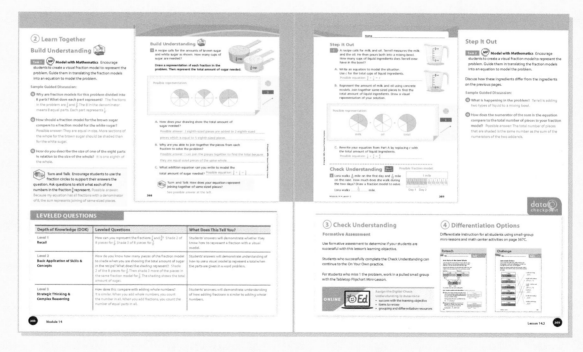

Leveled Questions and Sample Guided Instruction features help teachers ask questions that facilitate student understanding without giving away the answer.

Teacher Support

Empowering Teachers

Into Math is designed to provide opportunities for each and every student to grow. Formative assessment and effective differentiation are critical to student success. However, care must be taken not to turn classrooms into unintentional tracking systems, which often create gates instead of gateways. Access to effective teaching and learning, a high-quality curriculum, and high expectations promote equitable math classrooms.

Professional Learning Cards help teachers effectively implement the Talk Moves and Language Routines, ensuring student reasoning and discourse play a key role in instruction.

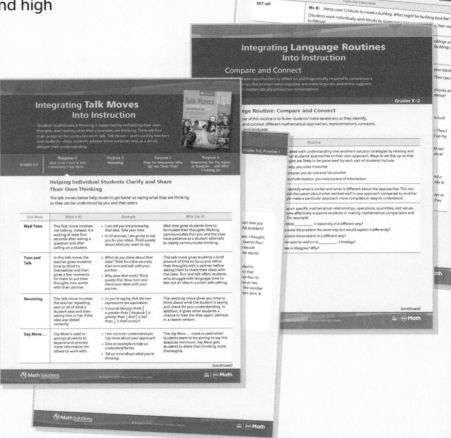

Talk Moves

- Adding On
- Reasoning
- Repeating
- Revoicing
- Turn and Talk
- Waiting

Language Routines

- Three Reads
- Critique, Correct, and Clarify
- Stronger and Clearer Each Time
- Compare and Connect

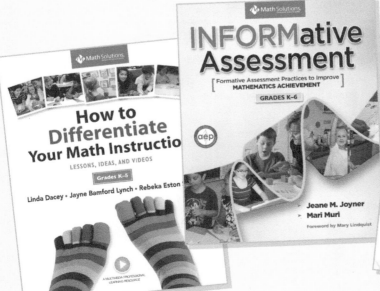

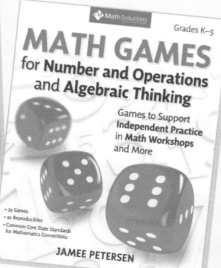

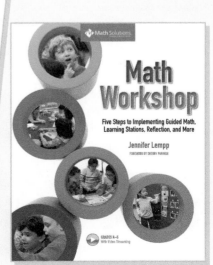

Math Solutions professional learning publications, available to enhance your professional library, are referenced in the *Into Math* Teacher Edition.

Matthew R. Larson, PhD
Past President National Council of
Teachers of Mathematics
Lincoln Public Schools
Lincoln, Nebraska
Math Solutions Senior Fellow

Ensuring Access and Equity

Access

Access and equity are a guiding principle of effective mathematics programs in which each and every student has access to effective instruction, high expectations, high-quality curriculum, and the support necessary to learn mathematics at a deep level (NCTM, 2014). *Into Math* provides the structure and resources needed to effectively differentiate instruction and support student learning.

The *Into Math* curriculum is rigorous and supports students' conceptual understanding, procedural fluency, and reasoning and problem-solving abilities through an intentional lesson and module design. *Into Math*'s frequent and embedded data checkpoints—linked to targeted instructional supports in print, digital, small-group, and math center options—are designed to ensure that each and every student has access to *Into Math*'s high-quality curriculum.

Equitable Instructional Practices

Mathematics teaching involves more than helping students acquire concepts and skills; it also includes supporting students in coming to see themselves as capable of learning, participating in, and becoming users of mathematics. Implementing equitable instructional practices can improve students' classroom experiences, learning outcomes, and dispositions toward mathematics.

The mathematics teaching practices included in *Into Math* provide an instructional framework for cultivating students' confidence and belief in their ability to learn and use mathematics. For example, the tasks in Spark Your Learning are designed as "low-floor/high-ceiling" tasks that all students can access but that can also be extended to provide challenge. These tasks motivate learning, focus on building students' conceptual understanding to help ensure procedural fluency, encourage the use of multiple representations, and help students develop a positive disposition toward mathematics and themselves as learners.

Similarly, Turn and Talk prompts position students as mathematically competent and capable of sharing their thinking and participating in mathematical arguments. Through discourse, students realize that their thinking serves an important role in learning mathematics and cultivate their confidence as learners,[1] which, in turn, improves the learning outcomes of each and every student.

 Turn and Talk How are the divisor, dividend, and quotient used to represent the number of groups and the size of each group in this situation?

---

1) D. Huinker & V. Bill, Taking Action: Implementing Effective Mathematics Teaching Practices in K–Grade 5, ed. M. S. Smith (Reston, VA: NCTM, 2017).

Teacher Support

Building a Culture of Professional Growth

A blend of in-person and online support with Math Solutions® coaches fosters a culture of professional growth and inspires a culture of math achievement with every student, in every classroom, every day.

Coaches from Math Solutions® will work side by side with teachers to develop instructional practices that promote reasoning and problem-solving skills. Our goal is to support teachers as they create learning environments where students are encouraged to become fearless problem solvers.

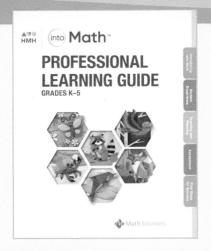

During the *Getting Started with Into Math* session, teachers receive a Professional Learning Guide. The Professional Learning Guide is also available on Ed: Your Friend in Learning.

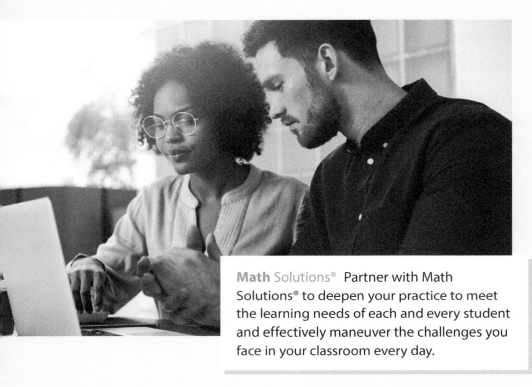

Math Solutions® Partner with Math Solutions® to deepen your practice to meet the learning needs of each and every student and effectively maneuver the challenges you face in your classroom every day.

Getting Started Modules can be accessed anywhere and anytime on Ed: Your Friend in Learning.

The single greatest determinant for success in a classroom is the teacher. Math Solutions® coaches partner with you as you make critical decisions that impact student learning.

Weston Kieschnick
Associate Partner
International Center for
Leadership in Education
Littleton, Colorado

Blended Learning That Works

Purposeful Technology Use + Old-School Wisdom

We know that digital tools and future-focused learning environments are critical when preparing our students for the real world. But what about the tried-and-true teaching strategies that have always driven real and measurable learning? Where do these fit in?

The Bold School Framework for Strategic Blended Learning™ puts teachers back into the digital learning equation. Its practical yet powerful approach shows how purposeful technology use combined with old-school wisdom can elevate instruction and enhance learning.

Effective 21st-century learning blends sound pedagogical practices with digital elements to create engaging rigorous and relevant experiences. As educators, we are accountable for the learning outcomes and career readiness of our students. Technology and digital tools, when implemented strategically to enhance—not replace—sound pedagogy, create effective and efficient blended learning experiences for students. Here's how it works.

Bold School Framework for Strategic Blended Learning™	
Step 1	Identify Desired Academic Outcome(s)
Step 2	Select a Goal-Aligned Instructional Strategy That *Works*
Step 3	Choose Digital Tool(s)
Step 4	Plan Blended Instruction
Step 5	Self-Assess Your Plans and Progress with a Framework

The goal of using technology isn't just to use technology—it's student achievement. We must approach blended learning with greater intention than just "What am I going to do with (insert tech tool here) today?" With this mindset, every teacher can support students through the power of digital learning.

Fostering Learning Mindsets

Through a partnership with Mindset Works®, *Into Math* incorporates the latest research, strategies, and practices to build a community of resilient, curious learners.

- Introduce the learning mindsets—growth mindset, relevance, belonging, and purpose—to help students better understand their self perception and attitudes toward learning.

- Establish the tenets of growth mindset, so that each student understands that he or she has the capacity to learn and grow.

- Target the research-based stances and skills that are key to student agency, engagement, and academic success.

Connect with Families and Community

Engaging with families and the community is critical to student success in school. *Into Math* provides resources to help teachers interact with families throughout the school year.

- **Math on the Spot** video tutorials provide instruction of the math concepts covered and allow for family involvement in their child's learning. The write-in format of the Student Edition gives families a front-row seat to their child's thinking and progress over time, encouraging a strong home-school connection.

- **School Home Letters** inform families about the skills, strategies, and topics students are encountering at school, extending rich dialogue beyond the classroom.

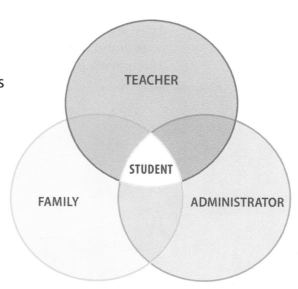

David Dockterman, EdD
Lecturer, Harvard Graduate
School of Education
Cambridge, Massachusetts

Understanding Mindset

Into Math fosters a growth mindset by explicitly teaching students that intelligence is not a fixed trait, but rather hard work and determination are crucial factors in raising academic achievement. Students often believe that their ability to excel in mathematics is fixed. Carol Dweck, a psychologist at Stanford University and leading researcher in student motivation and development, highlights the academic benefits of adopting a "growth" mindset rather than a "fixed" mindset.

Growth Mindset

Growth mindset is the idea that intelligence and abilities can be developed through dedication and work. "This view creates a drive towards learning and a resilience that is essential for great accomplishment. Virtually all great people have had these qualities."[1] Instruction and classroom community can foster a growth mindset by explicitly teaching that effort has a meaningful impact on learning.[2] Students with a growth mindset believe:

- Practice and effort are key elements in developing intelligence.
- Persistence and perseverance are important factors in triumphing over setbacks and failures.
- Mistakes and struggle are part of the learning process.

Fixed Mindset

Students who have a fixed mindset believe that intelligence and abilities are fixed traits that cannot be developed. Students who view their intelligence as fixed from birth are more likely to experience decreased confidence and performance when faced with challenges.[3] Students with a fixed mindset

- believe intelligence is a fixed quantity that you either possess or lack,
- put in less effort and give up easily, and
- fear failure and are less likely to take risks.

Teaching Growth Mindset

Feedback and classroom discourse can have a lasting impact on how students view intelligence.[4] By adopting a growth mindset and productive learning strategies, students are more likely to step up to challenges and persevere through and bounce back from adversity. Use the following strategies:

- Teach that intelligence and abilities are developed.
- Praise students' efforts and strategies rather than their intelligence.
- Use "mistakes" or incorrect answers as teachable moments.

1) C. Dweck, *Mindset: The New Psychology of Success*. (New York, NY: Penguin Random House, 2006).

2) L. S. Blackwell, K. H. Trzesniewski, C. S. Dweck, "Theories of Intelligence Predict Achievement Across an Adolescent Transition: A Longitudinal Study and an Intervention," *Child Development* 78, no. 1 (January-February 2007): 246–263.

3) Blackwell, Trzesniewski, Dweck, "Theories of Intelligence . . . ," 246–263.

4) M. Malmivuori, "Affect and Self-Regulation," *Educational Studies in Mathematics* 63, no. 2 (October 2006): 149–164.

Teacher Support

Unpacking Math Standards

Into Math is built on a carefully crafted Learning Spine based on the Mathematics Standards, with a coherent progression from kindergarten through algebra and beyond. The *Into Math* system allows for easy access forward or backward across the K–12 Mathematical Progressions, providing teachers with the tools to navigate prerequisite and follow-on concepts and skills.

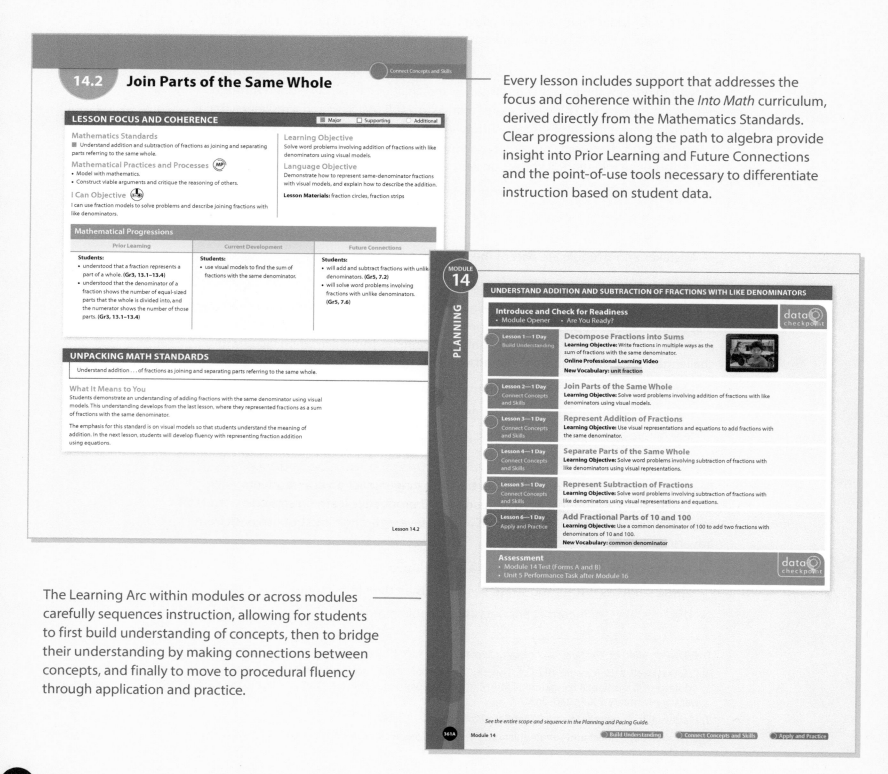

Every lesson includes support that addresses the focus and coherence within the *Into Math* curriculum, derived directly from the Mathematics Standards. Clear progressions along the path to algebra provide insight into Prior Learning and Future Connections and the point-of-use tools necessary to differentiate instruction based on student data.

The Learning Arc within modules or across modules carefully sequences instruction, allowing for students to first build understanding of concepts, then to bridge their understanding by making connections between concepts, and finally to move to procedural fluency through application and practice.

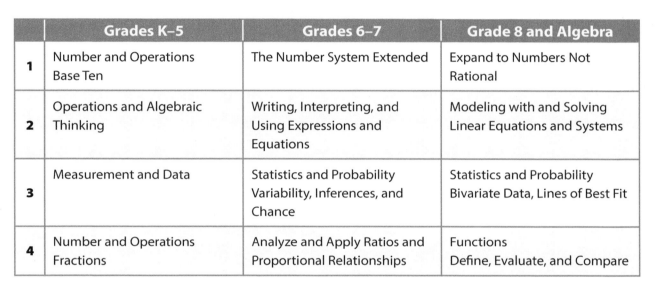

Timothy D. Kanold, PhD
Mathematics Educator
Chicago, Illinois

Progressions and Algebra Readiness

Algebra Readiness in 2020 and Beyond

Algebra as a course of study today is integrated around four progressions of elementary and middle school content leading to the algebra course: Number and Operations, Operations and Algebraic Thinking, Statistics and Probability, and Functions.

	Grades K–5	Grades 6–7	Grade 8 and Algebra
1	Number and Operations Base Ten	The Number System Extended	Expand to Numbers Not Rational
2	Operations and Algebraic Thinking	Writing, Interpreting, and Using Expressions and Equations	Modeling with and Solving Linear Equations and Systems
3	Measurement and Data	Statistics and Probability Variability, Inferences, and Chance	Statistics and Probability Bivariate Data, Lines of Best Fit
4	Number and Operations Fractions	Analyze and Apply Ratios and Proportional Relationships	Functions Define, Evaluate, and Compare

The Operations and Algebraic Thinking progression strand is unique to the K–5 preparation for the algebra readiness curriculum.

The Operations and Algebraic Thinking Progression

Operations and Algebraic Thinking is a K–5 progression that feeds directly into the middle school progression for linear expressions and equations.

At grade levels K–2, this progression focuses on counting, place value, and addition and subtraction of whole numbers. The emphasis is on representing and solving Add To, Take From, Put Together/Take Apart, and Compare problem situations for addition and subtraction. This work will help students to "see" multiplication as groups of objects and as represented by a rectangular array or model in Grades 3–5. Conceptual building blocks are developed for the eventual multiplication of whole numbers.

At grade levels 3–5, this progression expands into the conceptual student understanding needed for students to "see" patterns, properties, and expressions in problem situations—the early foundations of what will become known as algebra. These progressions include multiplication and division problem situations with equal groups, arrays, area, and comparisons. Third graders focus on fluency when multiplying and dividing within 100, fourth graders analyze shape and number patterns, and fifth graders use problem situations that allow them to both write and interpret numerical expressions based on earlier student work with whole numbers.

Teacher Support

Supporting Intervention Needs

Into Math provides the supports teachers need to ensure each and every student succeeds. Data informs teachers' use of differentiated Small-Group and Math Center options in every lesson. *Into Math* includes intervention content for use in a core classroom.

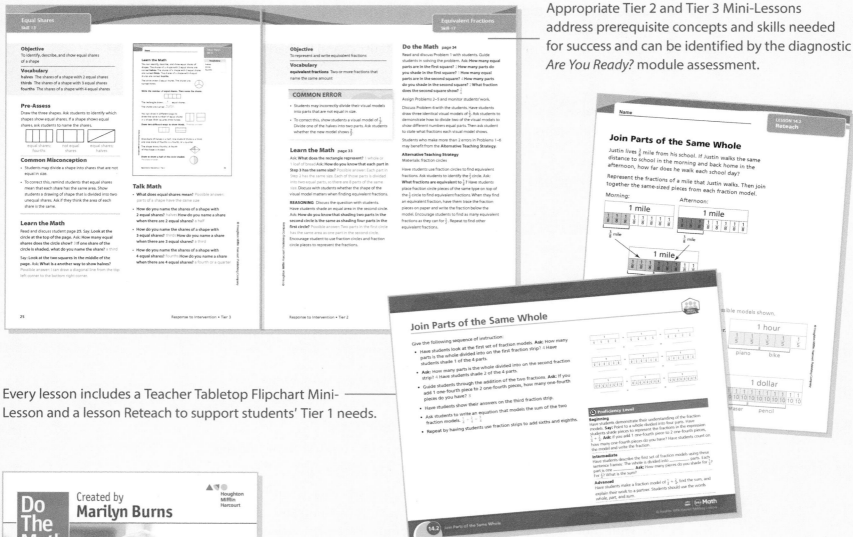

Appropriate Tier 2 and Tier 3 Mini-Lessons address prerequisite concepts and skills needed for success and can be identified by the diagnostic *Are You Ready?* module assessment.

Every lesson includes a Teacher Tabletop Flipchart Mini-Lesson and a lesson Reteach to support students' Tier 1 needs.

Created by Marilyn Burns

Houghton Mifflin Harcourt

Do The Math

HMH also offers robust Intervention Solutions for students who need targeted and intensive intervention. Developed by Marilyn Burns, *Do The Math* has thirteen modules that are organized into four topics—Addition and Subtraction, Multiplication, Division, and Fractions. These modules provide carefully scaffolded instruction to build conceptual understanding and develop numerical reasoning. See pages PG82–PG84.

- grades 1 and up
- can be used during core instruction or in a separate instruction block
- effective and easily managed instruction with embedded assessments
- includes digital resources
- six weeks of 30-minute lessons in each module

Foundational Research

Hattie, J., Fisher, D., & Frey, N. (2017). *Visible Learning for Mathematics: What Works Best to Optimize Student Learning*. Thousand Oaks, CA: Corwin.

National Council of Teachers of Mathematics (NCTM). (2014). *Principles to Actions: Ensuring Mathematical Success for All*. Reston, VA: NCTM.

National Research Council. Kilpatrick, J., Swafford, J., & Findell, B. (Eds.), (2001). *Adding It Up: Helping Children Learn Mathematics*. Washington, DC: National Academy Press.

National Research Council. (2005). *How Students Learn: Mathematics in the Classroom*. Washington, DC: National Academies Press.

Schielack, J., Charles, R., Clements, D., Duckett, P., Fennell, F. (Skip)., Lewandowski, S., Trevino, E., Zbiek, R.M., (2006). *Curriculum Focal Points for Prekindergarten through Grade 8 Mathematics*. Reston, VA: NCTM.

Curriculum Design and Standards

Common Core Standards Writing Team. (2013). *Progressions for the Common Core State Standards Mathematics*

National Board for Professional Teaching Standards. (2010, preface rev. 2015, 2016). *Mathematics Standards for Teachers of Students Ages 11–18+*. Arlington, VA: National Board for Professional Teaching Standards.

National Governors Association Center for Best Practices, Council of Chief State School Officers. (2012). *Common Core State Standards: K-8 Publisher's Criteria for the Common Core State Standards for Mathematics*. Washington, DC: National Governors Association Center for Best Practices, Council of Chief State School Officers.

Mathematics Knowledge for Teaching

Ball, D.L., Thames, M. H., & Phelps, G. (2008). Content knowledge for Teaching: What Makes It Special?. *Journal of Teacher Education, 59*(5), 389-407.

Chapin, S. H., O'Connor, C., & Anderson, N. C. (2013). *Classroom Discussions in Math: A Teacher's Guide for Using Talk Moves to Support the Common Core and more, Grades K-6* (3rd edition). Sausalito, CA: Math Solutions.

Chapin, S .H., & Johnson, A. (2000). *Math Matters: Understanding the Math You Teach. Grades K-6*. Sausalito, CA: Math Solutions.

Dean, C.B., Hubbell, E.R., Pitler, H., & Stone, B.J. (2nd ed., 2012). *Classroom Instruction that Works: Research-Based Strategies for Increasing Student Achievement*. Alexandria, VA: Association for Supervision and Curriculum Development.

Dixon, J.K., Nolan, E.C., Adams, T.L., Brooks, L.A., Howse, T.D. (2016). *Making Sense of Mathematics for Teaching Grades K-2*. Bloomington, IN: Solution Tree Press.

Dixon, J.K., Nolan, E.C., Adams, T.L., Tobias, J.M., Barmoha, G. (2016). *Making Sense of Mathematics for Teaching Grades 3-5*. Bloomington, IN: Solution Tree Press.

Hill, H. C., Ball, D. L., & Schilling, S. G. (2008). Unpacking Pedagogical Content Knowledge: Conceptualizing and Measuring Teachers' Topic-Specific Knowledge of Students. *Journal for Research in Mathematics Education, 39*(4), 372-400.

Huinker, D., & Bill, V. Smith, M.S. (Ed), (2017). *Taking Action: Implementing Effective Mathematics Teaching Practices in K-Grade 5*. Reston VA: NCTM.

Ma, L. (2nd ed., 2010). *Knowing and Teaching Elementary Mathematics: Teachers' Understanding of Fundamental Mathematics in China and the United States*. New York, NY: Routledge.

Nolan, E.C., Dixon, J.K., Roy, G.J., Andreasen, J.B. (2016). *Making Sense of Mathematics for Teaching Grades 6-8*. Bloomington, IN: Solution Tree Press.

Nolan, E.C., Dixon, J.K., Safi, F., Haciomeroglu, E.S. (2016). *Making Sense of Mathematics for Teaching High School*. Bloomington, IN: Solution Tree Press.

Petersen, J. (2013). *Math Games for Number and Operations and Algebraic Thinking: Games to Support Independent Practice in Math Workshops and More, Grades K-5*. Sausalito, CA: Math Solutions.

Schoenfeld, A. H. (2014). What Makes for Powerful Classrooms, and How Can We Support Teachers in Creating Them? A Story of Research and Practice, Productively Intertwined. *Educational Researcher, 43*(8), 404-412.

Shulman, L. S. (1986/2013). Those Who Understand: Knowledge Growth in Teaching. *The Journal of Education, 193*(3), 1-11.

Smith, M.S., & Stein, M.K. (2nd ed., 2018). *Five Practices for Orchestrating Productive Mathematical Discussion*. Thousand Oaks, CA: Corwin.

Steele, M., & Raith, M.L. Smith, M.S. (Ed), (2017). *Taking Action: Implementing Effective Mathematics Teaching Practices in Grades 6-8*. Reston VA: NCTM.

Differentiation

Dacey, L., Lynch, J. B., & Salemi, R. E. (2013). *How to Differentiate Your Math Instruction: Lessons, Ideas, and Videos with Common Core Support*. Sausalito, CA: Math Solutions.

Small, M. (3rd ed., 2017). *Good Questions: Great Ways to Differentiate Mathematics Instruction in the Standards-Based Classroom*. New York, NY: Teachers College Press.

English Language Learners

Council of the Great City Schools. (2014). *A Framework for Raising Expectations and Instructional Rigor for English Language Learners*.

National Council of Teachers of Mathematics (NCTM). Civil, M., & Turner, E. (Eds), (2014). *The Common Core State Standards in Mathematics for English Language Learners: Grades K-8*. Alexandria, VA: TESOL Press.

Zwiers, J., Dieckmann, J., Rutherford-Quach, S., Daro, V., Skarin, R., Weiss, S., & Malamut, J. (2017). *Principles for the Design of Mathematics Curricula: Promoting Language and Content Development*. Stanford, CA: Stanford University.

Continued on next page →

Professional Learning References

Equity

Aguirre, J., Mayfield-Ingram, K., Martin, D. (2013). *The Impact of Identity in K-8 Mathematics: Rethinking Equity-Based Practices.* Reston, VA: The National Council of Teachers of Mathematics.

Boaler, J., & Staples, M. (2008). Creating Mathematical Futures through an Equitable Teaching Approach: The Case of Railside School. *Teachers College Record,* 110(3), 608-645.

Flores, A. (2007). Examining Disparities in Mathematics Education: Achievement Gap or Opportunity Gap?. *High School Journal,* 91(1), 29-42.

Howard, T. C. (2010). *Why Race and Culture Matter in Schools: Closing the Achievement Gap in America's Classrooms* (2009). New York, NY: Teachers College Press.

Larson, M. R., & Andrews, D. (2015). One District's Journey to Promote Access and Equity. *New England Mathematics Journal,* XLVII, 31-40.

Leinwand, S. (2009). *Accessible Mathematics: 10 Instructional Shifts that Raise Student Achievement.* Portsmouth, NH: Heinemann.

Learning Mindset

Boaler, Jo (2016). *Mathematical Mindsets: Unleashing Students' Potential through Creative Math, Inspiring Messages and Innovative Teaching.* San Francisco, CA: Jossey-Bass.

Dockterman, D., & Blackwell, L. (2014). Growth Mindset in Context: Content and Culture Matter Too. *International Center for Leadership in Education,* 1-4.

Dweck, C. S. (2006). *Mindset: The New Psychology of Success.* New York, N.Y.: Penguin Random House.

Digital Learning Environment

Delgado, A.J., Wardlow, L., McKnight, K., & O'Malley, K. (2015). Educational Technology: A Review of the Integration, Resources, and Effectiveness of Technology in K-12 Classrooms. *Journal of Information Technology Education: Research,* 14, 397-416.

Imbriale, R. (2013). Blended Learning. *Principal Leadership,* 13(6), 30-34.

Kieschnick, W. (2017). International Center forLeadership in Education, Inc. *Bold School: Old School Wisdom + New School Technologies = Blended Learning that Works.* Rexford, NY.

Mayer, R. E. (2013). Multimedia Learning. In *Educational Psychology Handbook: International Guide to Student Achievement,* J. Hattie & E. Anderman (Eds.). 396-398. New York, N.Y.: Routledge.

Modern Teacher. (2016). *Digital Convergence: The Path Toward the K-12 Modern Learning Environment.* Denver, CO: Modern Teacher.

Public Impact. (2013). *A Better Blend: A Vision for Boosting Student Outcomes with Digital Learning.* Chapel Hill, NC: Public Impact.

Ross, S.M., Morrison, G.R., & Lowther, D.L. (2010). Educational Technology Research Past and Present: Balancing Rigor and Relevance to Impact School Learning. *Contemporary Educational Technology,* 1(1), 17-35.

Schneider, M.C., Egan, K.L., & Julian, M.W. (2013). Classroom Assessment in the Context of High-Stakes Testing. In *SAGE Handbook of Research on Classroom Assessment,* J. McMillan (Ed.). 55-70. Thousand Oaks, CA: SAGE.

U.S. Department of Education, Office of Planning, Evaluation, and Policy Development. (2009). *Evaluation of Evidence-Based Practices in Online Learning: A Meta-Analysis and Review of Online Learning Studies.* Washington, DC: U.S. Department of Education.

Assessment, Data, & Reports

Black, P., & Wiliam, D. (1998). Inside the Black Box: Raising Standards through Classroom Assessment. *Phi Delta Kappan,* 80(2), 139-144.

Popham, W. J. (8th ed., 2018). *Classroom Assessment: What Teachers Need to Know.* London: Pearson.

Stiggins, R. (2008). *Assessment Manifesto: A Call for the Development of Balanced Assessment Systems.* Portland, OR: ETS Assessment Training Institute.

Professional Learning

Darling-Hammond, L., Wei, R.C., Andree, A., Richardson, N., & Orphanos, S. (2009). *Professional Learning in the Learning Profession: A Status Report on Teacher Development in the United States and Abroad.* Oxford, OH: National Staff Development Council.

Dixon, J. K., Egendoerfer, L. A., & Clements, T. (2009). Do They Really Need to Raise Their Hands? Challenging a Traditional Social Norm in a Second Grade Mathematics Classroom. *Teaching and Teacher Education,* 25(8), 1067-1076.

Garet, M.S., Porter, A.C., Desimone, L., Birman, B.F., & Yoon, K.S. (2001). What Makes Professional Development Effective? Results from a National Sample of Teachers. *American Educational Research Journal,* 38(4), 915-945.

Hargreaves, A., & Fullan, M. (2013). The Power of Professional Capital: With an Investment in Collaboration, Teachers become Nation Builders. *Journal of Staff Development,* 34(3), 36-39.

Kanold, T.D., Kanold-McIntyre, J., Larson, M.R., Barnes, B., Schuhl, S., & Toncheff, M. (2018). *Mathematics Instruction & Tasks in a PLC at Work.* Bloomington, IN: Solution Tree Press.

Kelemanik, G., Lucenta, A., & Janssen Creighton, S. (2016). *Routines for Reasoning: Fostering the Mathematical Practices in All Students.* Portsmouth, NH: Heinemann.

Knight, J. (2007). *Instructional Coaching: A Partnership Approach to Improving Instruction.* Thousand Oaks, CA: Corwin.

Leinwand, S. (2nd ed., 2012) *Sensible Mathematics.* Portsmouth, NH: Heinemann.

Sweeney, D. (2011) *Student-Centered Coaching.* Thousand Oaks, CA: Corwin Press.

Notes & Reflections

Pacing Guide

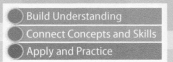

Lesson	Mathematics Standards, Grade 4	Pacing
Unit 1 PLACE VALUE AND WHOLE-NUMBER OPERATIONS		
Module 1: Place Value of Whole Numbers		
Lesson 1.1 Understand Place Value Relationships	■ Recognize that in a multi-digit whole number, a digit in one place represents ten times what it represents in the place to its right.	2 days
Lesson 1.2 Read and Write Numbers	■ Read and write multi-digit whole numbers using base-ten numerals, number names, and expanded form. Compare two multi-digit numbers based on meanings of the digits in each place, using >, =, and < symbols to record the results of comparisons.	1 day
Lesson 1.3 Regroup and Rename Numbers	■ Recognize that in a multi-digit whole number, a digit in one place represents ten times what it represents in the place to its right.	1 day
Lesson 1.4 Compare and Order Numbers	■ Read and write multi-digit whole numbers using base-ten numerals, number names, and expanded form. Compare two multi-digit numbers based on meanings of the digits in each place, using >, =, and < symbols to record the results of comparisons.	1 day
Lesson 1.5 Use Place Value Understanding to Round Numbers	■ Use place value understanding to round multi-digit whole numbers to any place.	1 day
Module 2: Addition and Subtraction of Whole Numbers		
Lesson 2.1 Add Whole Numbers and Assess Reasonableness	■ Fluently add and subtract multi-digit whole numbers using the standard algorithm.	1 day
Lesson 2.2 Subtract Whole Numbers and Assess Reasonableness	■ Fluently add and subtract multi-digit whole numbers using the standard algorithm.	1 day
Lesson 2.3 Use Addition and Subtraction to Solve Comparison Problems	■ Fluently add and subtract multi-digit whole numbers using the standard algorithm.	1 day
Lesson 2.4 Apply the Perimeter Formula for Rectangles	☐ Apply the area and perimeter formulas for rectangles in real world and mathematical problems.	1 day
Unit 2 MULTIPLICATION AND DIVISION PROBLEMS		
Module 3: Interpret and Solve Problem Situations		
Lesson 3.1 Explore Multiplicative Comparisons	■ Interpret a multiplication equation as a comparison, e.g., interpret $35 = 5 \times 7$ as a statement that 35 is 5 times as many as 7 and 7 times as many as 5. Represent verbal statements of multiplicative comparisons as multiplication equations.	1 day
	■ Multiply or divide to solve word problems involving multiplicative comparison, e.g., by using drawings and equations with a symbol for the unknown number to represent the problem, distinguishing multiplicative comparison from additive comparison.	
Lesson 3.2 Distinguish Between Multiplicative and Additive Comparisons	■ Multiply or divide to solve word problems involving multiplicative comparison, e.g., by using drawings and equations with a symbol for the unknown number to represent the problem, distinguishing multiplicative comparison from additive comparison.	1 day

■ Major
□ Supporting
○ Additional

In addition to the core instructional pacing, HMH recommends the following:
• 3 days per year for the Growth Measure assessments
• 2 days per module for the Module Opener, Are You Ready?, Module Review, and Module Test
• 1 day per unit for the Performance Task
Using these recommendations, the total pacing for Grade 4 is 170 days.

Lesson		Mathematics Standards, Grade 4	Pacing
Lesson 3.3 Use Division to Solve Multiplicative Comparison Problems	■	Multiply or divide to solve word problems involving multiplicative comparison, e.g., by using drawings and equations with a symbol for the unknown number to represent the problem, distinguishing multiplicative comparison from additive comparison.	1 day
Lesson 3.4 Use Comparisons to Solve Problem Situations	■	Multiply or divide to solve word problems involving multiplicative comparison, e.g., by using drawings and equations with a symbol for the unknown number to represent the problem, distinguishing multiplicative comparison from additive comparison.	1 day
Lesson 3.5 Solve Multistep Problems with Multiplication and Division	■	Multiply or divide to solve word problems involving multiplicative comparison, e.g., by using drawings and equations with a symbol for the unknown number to represent the problem, distinguishing multiplicative comparison from additive comparison.	1 day
	■	Solve multistep word problems posed with whole numbers and having whole-number answers using the four operations, including problems in which remainders must be interpreted. Represent these problems using equations with a letter standing for the unknown quantity. Assess the reasonableness of answers using mental computation and estimation strategies including rounding.	
Module 4: Mental Math and Estimation Strategies			
Lesson 4.1 Explore Multiplication Patterns with Tens, Hundreds, and Thousands	■	Multiply a whole number of up to four digits by a one-digit whole number, and multiply two two-digit numbers, using strategies based on place value and the properties of operations. Illustrate and explain the calculation by using equations, rectangular arrays, and/or area models.	1 day
Lesson 4.2 Explore Division Patterns with Tens, Hundreds, and Thousands	■	Find whole-number quotients and remainders with up to four-digit dividends and one-digit divisors, using strategies based on place value, the properties of operations, and/or the relationship between multiplication and division. Illustrate and explain the calculation by using equations, rectangular arrays, and/or area models.	1 day
Lesson 4.3 Estimate Products by 1-Digit Numbers	■	Use place value understanding to round multi-digit whole numbers to any place.	1 day
	■	Multiply a whole number of up to four digits by a one-digit whole number, and multiply two two-digit numbers, using strategies based on place value and the properties of operations. Illustrate and explain the calculation by using equations, rectangular arrays, and/or area models.	
Lesson 4.4 Estimate Quotients Using Compatible Numbers	■	Find whole-number quotients and remainders with up to four-digit dividends and one-digit divisors, using strategies based on place value, the properties of operations, and/or the relationship between multiplication and division. Illustrate and explain the calculation by using equations, rectangular arrays, and/or area models.	1 day

Module continued on next page →

Pacing Guide

- Build Understanding
- Connect Concepts and Skills
- Apply and Practice

Lesson	Mathematics Standards, Grade 4	Pacing
Module 4: Mental Math and Estimation Strategies		
Lesson 4.5 Use Mental Math Strategies for Multiplication and Division	■ Multiply a whole number of up to four digits by a one-digit whole number, and multiply two two-digit numbers, using strategies based on place value and the properties of operations. Illustrate and explain the calculation by using equations, rectangular arrays, and/or area models. ■ Find whole-number quotients and remainders with up to four-digit dividends and one-digit divisors, using strategies based on place value, the properties of operations, and/or the relationship between multiplication and division. Illustrate and explain the calculation by using equations, rectangular arrays, and/or area models.	1 day
Module 5: Multiply by 1-Digit Numbers		
Lesson 5.1 Represent Multiplication	■ Multiply a whole number of up to four digits by a one-digit whole number, and multiply two two-digit numbers, using strategies based on place value and the properties of operations. Illustrate and explain the calculation by using equations, rectangular arrays, and/or area models.	1 day
Lesson 5.2 Use Area Models and the Distributive Property to Multiply	■ Multiply a whole number of up to four digits by a one-digit whole number, and multiply two two-digit numbers, using strategies based on place value and the properties of operations. Illustrate and explain the calculation by using equations, rectangular arrays, and/or area models.	1 day
Lesson 5.3 Multiply Using Expanded Form	■ Multiply a whole number of up to four digits by a one-digit whole number, and multiply two two-digit numbers, using strategies based on place value and the properties of operations. Illustrate and explain the calculation by using equations, rectangular arrays, and/or area models.	1 day
Lesson 5.4 Multiply Using Partial Products	■ Multiply a whole number of up to four digits by a one-digit whole number, and multiply two two-digit numbers, using strategies based on place value and the properties of operations. Illustrate and explain the calculation by using equations, rectangular arrays, and/or area models.	1 day
Lesson 5.5 Use Place Value to Multiply 2-Digit Numbers	■ Multiply a whole number of up to four digits by a one-digit whole number, and multiply two two-digit numbers, using strategies based on place value and the properties of operations. Illustrate and explain the calculation by using equations, rectangular arrays, and/or area models.	1 day
Lesson 5.6 Multiply 3-Digit and 4-Digit Numbers	■ Multiply a whole number of up to four digits by a one-digit whole number, and multiply two two-digit numbers, using strategies based on place value and the properties of operations. Illustrate and explain the calculation by using equations, rectangular arrays, and/or area models.	1 day
Lesson 5.7 Use Equations to Solve Multistep Problems	■ Solve multistep word problems posed with whole numbers and having whole-number answers using the four operations, including problems in which remainders must be interpreted. Represent these problems using equations with a letter standing for the unknown quantity. Assess the reasonableness of answers using mental computation and estimation strategies including rounding.	1 day

Lesson		Mathematics Standards, Grade 4	Pacing
Module 6: **Understand Division by 1-Digit Numbers**			
Lesson 6.1 Represent Division	■	Find whole-number quotients and remainders with up to four-digit dividends and one-digit divisors, using strategies based on place value, the properties of operations, and/or the relationship between multiplication and division. Illustrate and explain the calculation by using equations, rectangular arrays, and/or area models.	1 day
Lesson 6.2 Investigate Remainders	■	Find whole-number quotients and remainders with up to four-digit dividends and one-digit divisors, using strategies based on place value, the properties of operations, and/or the relationship between multiplication and division. Illustrate and explain the calculation by using equations, rectangular arrays, and/or area models.	1 day
Lesson 6.3 Interpret Remainders	■	Find whole-number quotients and remainders with up to four-digit dividends and one-digit divisors, using strategies based on place value, the properties of operations, and/or the relationship between multiplication and division. Illustrate and explain the calculation by using equations, rectangular arrays, and/or area models.	1 day
	■	Solve multistep word problems posed with whole numbers and having whole-number answers using the four operations, including problems in which remainders must be interpreted. Represent these problems using equations with a letter standing for the unknown quantity. Assess the reasonableness of answers using mental computation and estimation strategies including rounding.	
Lesson 6.4 Use Area Models and the Distributive Property to Divide	■	Find whole-number quotients and remainders with up to four-digit dividends and one-digit divisors, using strategies based on place value, the properties of operations, and/or the relationship between multiplication and division. Illustrate and explain the calculation by using equations, rectangular arrays, and/or area models.	1 day
Lesson 6.5 Divide Using Repeated Subtraction	■	Find whole-number quotients and remainders with up to four-digit dividends and one-digit divisors, using strategies based on place value, the properties of operations, and/or the relationship between multiplication and division. Illustrate and explain the calculation by using equations, rectangular arrays, and/or area models.	1 day
Lesson 6.6 Divide Using Partial Quotients	■	Find whole-number quotients and remainders with up to four-digit dividends and one-digit divisors, using strategies based on place value, the properties of operations, and/or the relationship between multiplication and division. Illustrate and explain the calculation by using equations, rectangular arrays, and/or area models.	1 day
Module 7: **Divide by 1-Digit Numbers**			
Lesson 7.1 Represent Division with Regrouping	■	Find whole-number quotients and remainders with up to four-digit dividends and one-digit divisors, using strategies based on place value, the properties of operations, and/or the relationship between multiplication and division. Illustrate and explain the calculation by using equations, rectangular arrays, and/or area models.	1 day

Module continued on next page →

Pacing Guide

Lesson		Mathematics Standards, Grade 4	Pacing
Module 7: **Divide by 1-Digit Numbers**			
Lesson 7.2 Use Place Value to Divide	■	Find whole-number quotients and remainders with up to four-digit dividends and one-digit divisors, using strategies based on place value, the properties of operations, and/or the relationship between multiplication and division. Illustrate and explain the calculation by using equations, rectangular arrays, and/or area models.	2 days
Lesson 7.3 Divide by 1-Digit Numbers	■	Find whole-number quotients and remainders with up to four-digit dividends and one-digit divisors, using strategies based on place value, the properties of operations, and/or the relationship between multiplication and division. Illustrate and explain the calculation by using equations, rectangular arrays, and/or area models.	1 day
Lesson 7.4 Solve Multistep Multiplication and Division Problems	■	Solve multistep word problems posed with whole numbers and having whole-number answers using the four operations, including problems in which remainders must be interpreted. Represent these problems using equations with a letter standing for the unknown quantity. Assess the reasonableness of answers using mental computation and estimation strategies including rounding.	1 day
Unit 3 **EXTEND AND APPLY MULTIPLICATION**			
Module 8: **Multiply by 2-Digit Numbers**			
Lesson 8.1 Multiply with Tens	■	Multiply a whole number of up to four digits by a one-digit whole number, and multiply two two-digit numbers, using strategies based on place value and the properties of operations. Illustrate and explain the calculation by using equations, rectangular arrays, and/or area models.	1 day
Lesson 8.2 Estimate Products	■	Use place value understanding to round multi-digit whole numbers to any place.	2 days
Lesson 8.3 Relate Area Models and Partial Products	■	Multiply a whole number of up to four digits by a one-digit whole number, and multiply two two-digit numbers, using strategies based on place value and the properties of operations. Illustrate and explain the calculation by using equations, rectangular arrays, and/or area models.	1 day
Lesson 8.4 Multiply Using Partial Products	■	Multiply a whole number of up to four digits by a one-digit whole number, and multiply two two-digit numbers, using strategies based on place value and the properties of operations. Illustrate and explain the calculation by using equations, rectangular arrays, and/or area models.	1 day
Lesson 8.5 Multiply with Regrouping	■	Multiply a whole number of up to four digits by a one-digit whole number, and multiply two two-digit numbers, using strategies based on place value and the properties of operations. Illustrate and explain the calculation by using equations, rectangular arrays, and/or area models.	1 day
Lesson 8.6 Choose a Multiplication Strategy	■	Multiply a whole number of up to four digits by a one-digit whole number, and multiply two two-digit numbers, using strategies based on place value and the properties of operations. Illustrate and explain the calculation by using equations, rectangular arrays, and/or area models.	1 day

Lesson		Mathematics Standards, Grade 4	Pacing
Lesson 8.7 Solve Multistep Problems and Assess Reasonableness	■	Solve multistep word problems posed with whole numbers and having whole-number answers using the four operations, including problems in which remainders must be interpreted. Represent these problems using equations with a letter standing for the unknown quantity. Assess the reasonableness of answers using mental computation and estimation strategies including rounding.	1 day
Module 9: Apply Multiplication to Area			
Lesson 9.1 Apply the Area Formula to Rectangles	☐	Apply the area and perimeter formulas for rectangles in real world and mathematical problems.	1 day
Lesson 9.2 Find the Area of Combined Rectangles	☐	Apply the area and perimeter formulas for rectangles in real world and mathematical problems.	1 day
Lesson 9.3 Find Unknown Measures	☐	Apply the area and perimeter formulas for rectangles in real world and mathematical problems.	1 day
Lesson 9.4 Solve Area Problems	☐	Apply the area and perimeter formulas for rectangles in real world and mathematical problems.	1 day
Unit 4 FRACTIONS AND DECIMALS			
Module 10: Algebraic Thinking: Number Theory			
Lesson 10.1 Investigate Factors	☐	Find all factor pairs for a whole number in the range 1–100. Recognize that a whole number is a multiple of each of its factors. Determine whether a given whole number in the range 1–100 is a multiple of a given one-digit number. Determine whether a given whole number in the range 1–100 is prime or composite.	1 day
Lesson 10.2 Identify Factors	☐	Find all factor pairs for a whole number in the range 1–100. Recognize that a whole number is a multiple of each of its factors. Determine whether a given whole number in the range 1–100 is a multiple of a given one-digit number. Determine whether a given whole number in the range 1–100 is prime or composite.	2 days
Lesson 10.3 Generate Multiples Using Factors	☐	Find all factor pairs for a whole number in the range 1–100. Recognize that a whole number is a multiple of each of its factors. Determine whether a given whole number in the range 1–100 is a multiple of a given one-digit number. Determine whether a given whole number in the range 1–100 is prime or composite.	1 day
Lesson 10.4 Identify Prime and Composite Numbers	☐	Find all factor pairs for a whole number in the range 1–100. Recognize that a whole number is a multiple of each of its factors. Determine whether a given whole number in the range 1–100 is a multiple of a given one-digit number. Determine whether a given whole number in the range 1–100 is prime or composite.	1 day
Lesson 10.5 Generate and Analyze Number Patterns	○	Generate a number or shape pattern that follows a given rule. Identify apparent features of the pattern that were not explicit in the rule itself.	1 day

Pacing Guide

Lesson	Mathematics Standards, Grade 4	Pacing
Module 11: Fraction Equivalence and Comparison		
Lesson 11.1 Compare Fractions Using Visual Models	■ Compare two fractions with different numerators and different denominators, e.g., by creating common denominators or numerators, or by comparing to a benchmark fraction such as 1/2. Recognize that comparisons are valid only when the two fractions refer to the same whole. Record the results of comparisons with symbols >, =, or <, and justify the conclusions, e.g., by using a visual fraction model.	1 day
Lesson 11.2 Compare Fractions Using Benchmarks	■ Compare two fractions with different numerators and different denominators, e.g., by creating common denominators or numerators, or by comparing to a benchmark fraction such as 1/2. Recognize that comparisons are valid only when the two fractions refer to the same whole. Record the results of comparisons with symbols >, =, or <, and justify the conclusions, e.g., by using a visual fraction model.	1 day
Lesson 11.3 Explain Fraction Equivalence Using Visual Models	■ Explain why a fraction a/b is equivalent to a fraction $(n \times a)/(n \times b)$ by using visual fraction models, with attention to how the number and size of the parts differ even though the two fractions themselves are the same size. Use this principle to recognize and generate equivalent fractions.	1 day
Lesson 11.4 Generate Equivalent Fractions	■ Explain why a fraction a/b is equivalent to a fraction $(n \times a)/(n \times b)$ by using visual fraction models, with attention to how the number and size of the parts differ even though the two fractions themselves are the same size. Use this principle to recognize and generate equivalent fractions.	1 day
Lesson 11.5 Use Common Multiples to Write Equivalent Fractions	■ Explain why a fraction a/b is equivalent to a fraction $(n \times a)/(n \times b)$ by using visual fraction models, with attention to how the number and size of the parts differ even though the two fractions themselves are the same size. Use this principle to recognize and generate equivalent fractions.	1 day
Lesson 11.6 Compare Fractions Using Common Numerators and Denominators	■ Compare two fractions with different numerators and different denominators, e.g., by creating common denominators or numerators, or by comparing to a benchmark fraction such as 1/2. Recognize that comparisons are valid only when the two fractions refer to the same whole. Record the results of comparisons with symbols >, =, or <, and justify the conclusions, e.g., by using a visual fraction model.	1 day
Lesson 11.7 Use Comparisons to Order Fractions	■ Compare two fractions with different numerators and different denominators, e.g., by creating common denominators or numerators, or by comparing to a benchmark fraction such as 1/2. Recognize that comparisons are valid only when the two fractions refer to the same whole. Record the results of comparisons with symbols >, =, or <, and justify the conclusions, e.g., by using a visual fraction model.	1 day
Module 12: Relate Fractions and Decimals		
Lesson 12.1 Represent Tenths as Fractions and Decimals	■ Use decimal notation for fractions with denominators 10 or 100.	1 day
Lesson 12.2 Represent Hundredths as Fractions and Decimals	■ Use decimal notation for fractions with denominators 10 or 100.	1 day

Lesson	Mathematics Standards, Grade 4	Pacing
Lesson 12.3 Identify Equivalent Fractions and Decimals	■ Express a fraction with denominator 10 as an equivalent fraction with denominator 100, and use this technique to add two fractions with respective denominators 10 and 100. ■ Use decimal notation for fractions with denominators 10 or 100.	1 day
Lesson 12.4 Compare Decimals	■ Compare two decimals to hundredths by reasoning about their size. Recognize that comparisons are valid only when the two decimals refer to the same whole. Record the results of comparisons with the symbols >, =, or <, and justify the conclusions, e.g., by using a visual model.	1 day
Lesson 12.5 Relate Fractions, Decimals, and Money	■ Use decimal notation for fractions with denominators 10 or 100.	1 day
Lesson 12.6 Solve Multistep Money Problems	☐ Use the four operations to solve word problems involving distances, intervals of time, liquid volumes, masses of objects, and money, including problems involving simple fractions or decimals, and problems that require expressing measurements given in a larger unit in terms of a smaller unit. Represent measurement quantities using diagrams such as number line diagrams that feature a measurement scale.	1 day

Module 13: Use Fractions to Understand Angles

Lesson	Mathematics Standards, Grade 4	Pacing
Lesson 13.1 Explore Lines, Rays, and Angles	○ Draw points, lines, line segments, rays, angles (right, acute, obtuse), and perpendicular and parallel lines. Identify these in two-dimensional figures.	1 day
Lesson 13.2 Explore Angles	○ Recognize angles as geometric shapes that are formed wherever two rays share a common endpoint, and understand concepts of angle measurement: An angle is measured with reference to a circle with its center at the common endpoint of the rays, by considering the fraction of the circular arc between the points where the two rays intersect the circle. An angle that turns through 1/360 of a circle is called a "one-degree angle," and can be used to measure angles.	1 day
Lesson 13.3 Relate Angles to Fractional Parts of a Circle	○ Recognize angles as geometric shapes that are formed wherever two rays share a common endpoint, and understand concepts of angle measurement: An angle is measured with reference to a circle with its center at the common endpoint of the rays, by considering the fraction of the circular arc between the points where the two rays intersect the circle. An angle that turns through 1/360 of a circle is called a "one-degree angle," and can be used to measure angles.	1 day
Lesson 13.4 Relate Degrees to Fractional Parts of Circles	○ Recognize angles as geometric shapes that are formed wherever two rays share a common endpoint, and understand concepts of angle measurement: An angle that turns through *n* one-degree angles is said to have an angle measure of *n* degrees. ○ Recognize angles as geometric shapes that are formed wherever two rays share a common endpoint, and understand concepts of angle measurement: An angle is measured with reference to a circle with its center at the common endpoint of the rays, by considering the fraction of the circular arc between the points where the two rays intersect the circle. An angle that turns through 1/360 of a circle is called a "one-degree angle," and can be used to measure angles.	2 days

Module continued on next page →

Pacing Guide

Lesson	Mathematics Standards, Grade 4	Pacing
Module 13: Use Fractions to Understand Angles		
Lesson 13.5 Measure and Draw Angles Using a Protractor	○ Measure angles in whole-number degrees using a protractor. Sketch angles of specified measure.	1 day
	○ Draw points, lines, line segments, rays, angles (right, acute, obtuse), and perpendicular and parallel lines. Identify these in two-dimensional figures.	
Lesson 13.6 Join and Separate Angles	○ Recognize angle measure as additive. When an angle is decomposed into non-overlapping parts, the angle measure of the whole is the sum of the angle measures of the parts. Solve addition and subtraction problems to find unknown angles on a diagram in real world and mathematical problems, e.g., by using an equation with a symbol for the unknown angle measure.	1 day
Lesson 13.7 Find Unknown Angle Measures	○ Recognize angle measure as additive. When an angle is decomposed into non-overlapping parts, the angle measure of the whole is the sum of the angle measures of the parts. Solve addition and subtraction problems to find unknown angles on a diagram in real world and mathematical problems, e.g., by using an equation with a symbol for the unknown angle measure.	1 day
Unit 5 OPERATIONS WITH FRACTIONS		
Module 14: Understand Addition and Subtraction of Fractions with Like Denominators		
Lesson 14.1 Decompose Fractions into Sums	■ Decompose a fraction into a sum of fractions with the same denominator in more than one way, recording each decomposition by an equation. Justify decompositions, e.g., by using a visual fraction model.	1 day
Lesson 14.2 Join Parts of the Same Whole	■ Understand addition and subtraction of fractions as joining and separating parts referring to the same whole.	1 day
Lesson 14.3 Represent Addition of Fractions	■ Solve word problems involving addition and subtraction of fractions referring to the same whole and having like denominators, e.g., by using visual fraction models and equations to represent the problem.	1 day
Lesson 14.4 Separate Parts of the Same Whole	■ Understand addition and subtraction of fractions as joining and separating parts referring to the same whole.	1 day
Lesson 14.5 Represent Subtraction of Fractions	■ Solve word problems involving addition and subtraction of fractions referring to the same whole and having like denominators, e.g., by using visual fraction models and equations to represent the problem.	1 day
Lesson 14.6 Add Fractional Parts of 10 and 100	■ Express a fraction with denominator 10 as an equivalent fraction with denominator 100, and use this technique to add two fractions with respective denominators 10 and 100.	1 day
Module 15: Add and Subtract Fractions and Mixed Numbers with Like Denominators		
Lesson 15.1 Add and Subtract Fractions to Solve Problems	■ Solve word problems involving addition and subtraction of fractions referring to the same whole and having like denominators, e.g., by using visual fraction models and equations to represent the problem.	1 day
Lesson 15.2 Rename Fractions and Mixed Numbers	■ Decompose a fraction into a sum of fractions with the same denominator in more than one way, recording each decomposition by an equation. Justify decompositions, e.g., by using a visual fraction model.	1 day

Lesson	Mathematics Standards, Grade 4	Pacing
Lesson 15.3 Add and Subtract Mixed Numbers to Solve Problems	■ Add and subtract mixed numbers with like denominators, e.g., by replacing each mixed number with an equivalent fraction, and/or by using properties of operations and the relationship between addition and subtraction.	2 days
Lesson 15.4 Rename Mixed Numbers to Subtract	■ Add and subtract mixed numbers with like denominators, e.g., by replacing each mixed number with an equivalent fraction, and/or by using properties of operations and the relationship between addition and subtraction.	1 day
Lesson 15.5 Apply Properties of Addition to Add Fractions and Mixed Numbers	■ Add and subtract mixed numbers with like denominators, e.g., by replacing each mixed number with an equivalent fraction, and/or by using properties of operations and the relationship between addition and subtraction.	1 day
Lesson 15.6 Practice Solving Fraction Problems	■ Solve word problems involving addition and subtraction of fractions referring to the same whole and having like denominators, e.g., by using visual fraction models and equations to represent the problem.	1 day
Module 16: Multiply Fractions by Whole Numbers		
Lesson 16.1 Understand Multiples of Unit Fractions	■ Understand a fraction a/b as a multiple of $1/b$.	1 day
Lesson 16.2 Find Multiples of Fractions	■ Understand a multiple of a/b as a multiple of $1/b$, and use this understanding to multiply a fraction by a whole number. ■ Solve word problems involving multiplication of a fraction by a whole number, e.g., by using visual fraction models and equations to represent the problem.	1 day
Lesson 16.3 Represent Multiplication of a Fraction by a Whole Number	■ Understand a multiple of a/b as a multiple of $1/b$, and use this understanding to multiply a fraction by a whole number. ■ Solve word problems involving multiplication of a fraction by a whole number, e.g., by using visual fraction models and equations to represent the problem.	2 days
Lesson 16.4 Solve Problems Using Multiplication of a Fraction or Mixed Number by a Whole Number	■ Solve word problems involving multiplication of a fraction by a whole number, e.g., by using visual fraction models and equations to represent the problem.	1 day
Unit 6 TWO-DIMENSIONAL FIGURES AND SYMMETRY		
Module 17: Two-Dimensional Figures		
Lesson 17.1 Identify and Draw Perpendicular and Parallel Lines	○ Draw points, lines, line segments, rays, angles (right, acute, obtuse), and perpendicular and parallel lines. Identify these in two-dimensional figures.	1 day

Module continued on next page →

Pacing Guide

Lesson	Mathematics Standards, Grade 4	Pacing
Module 17: Two-Dimensional Figures		
Lesson 17.2 Identify and Classify Triangles by Angles	○ Draw points, lines, line segments, rays, angles (right, acute, obtuse), and perpendicular and parallel lines. Identify these in two-dimensional figures.	1 day
	○ Classify two-dimensional figures based on the presence or absence of parallel or perpendicular lines, or the presence or absence of angles of a specified size. Recognize right triangles as a category, and identify right triangles.	
Lesson 17.3 Identify and Classify Triangles by Sides	○ Draw points, lines, line segments, rays, angles (right, acute, obtuse), and perpendicular and parallel lines. Identify these in two-dimensional figures.	1 day
	○ Classify two-dimensional figures based on the presence or absence of parallel or perpendicular lines, or the presence or absence of angles of a specified size. Recognize right triangles as a category, and identify right triangles.	
Lesson 17.4 Identify and Classify Quadrilaterals	○ Draw points, lines, line segments, rays, angles (right, acute, obtuse), and perpendicular and parallel lines. Identify these in two-dimensional figures.	1 day
	○ Classify two-dimensional figures based on the presence or absence of parallel or perpendicular lines, or the presence or absence of angles of a specified size. Recognize right triangles as a category, and identify right triangles.	
Lesson 17.5 Measure and Draw Angles of Two-Dimensional Figures	○ Draw points, lines, line segments, rays, angles (right, acute, obtuse), and perpendicular and parallel lines. Identify these in two-dimensional figures.	1 day
	○ Measure angles in whole-number degrees using a protractor. Sketch angles of specified measure.	
Module 18: Symmetry and Patterns		
Lesson 18.1 Recognize Lines of Symmetry	○ Recognize a line of symmetry for a two-dimensional figure as a line across the figure such that the figure can be folded along the line into matching parts. Identify line-symmetric figures and draw lines of symmetry.	1 day
Lesson 18.2 Identify and Draw Lines of Symmetry	○ Recognize a line of symmetry for a two-dimensional figure as a line across the figure such that the figure can be folded along the line into matching parts. Identify line-symmetric figures and draw lines of symmetry.	2 days
Lesson 18.3 Generate and Identify Shape Patterns	○ Generate a number or shape pattern that follows a given rule. Identify apparent features of the pattern that were not explicit in the rule itself.	1 day
Unit 7 MEASUREMENT, DATA, AND TIME		
Module 19: Relative Sizes of Customary Measurement Units		
Lesson 19.1 Identify Customary Measurement Benchmarks	☐ Know relative sizes of measurement units within one system of units including km, m, cm; kg, g; lb, oz.; l, ml; hr, min, sec. Within a single system of measurement, express measurements in a larger unit in terms of a smaller unit. Record measurement equivalents in a two-column table.	1 day

Lesson	Mathematics Standards, Grade 4	Pacing
Lesson 19.2 Compare Customary Units of Length	☐ Know relative sizes of measurement units within one system of units including km, m, cm; kg, g; lb, oz.; l, ml; hr, min, sec. Within a single system of measurement, express measurements in a larger unit in terms of a smaller unit. Record measurement equivalents in a two-column table.	2 days
Lesson 19.3 Compare Customary Units of Weight	☐ Know relative sizes of measurement units within one system of units including km, m, cm; kg, g; lb, oz.; l, ml; hr, min, sec. Within a single system of measurement, express measurements in a larger unit in terms of a smaller unit. Record measurement equivalents in a two-column table.	1 day
Lesson 19.4 Compare Customary Units of Liquid Volume	☐ Know relative sizes of measurement units within one system of units including km, m, cm; kg, g; lb, oz.; l, ml; hr, min, sec. Within a single system of measurement, express measurements in a larger unit in terms of a smaller unit. Record measurement equivalents in a two-column table.	1 day
Lesson 19.5 Represent and Interpret Measurement Data in Line Plots	☐ Make a line plot to display a data set of measurements in fractions of a unit (1/2, 1/4, 1/8). Solve problems involving addition and subtraction of fractions by using information presented in line plots. ☐ Use the four operations to solve word problems involving distances, intervals of time, liquid volumes, masses of objects, and money, including problems involving simple fractions or decimals, and problems that require expressing measurements given in a larger unit in terms of a smaller unit. Represent measurement quantities using diagrams such as number line diagrams that feature a measurement scale.	1 day
Module 20: Relative Sizes of Metric Measurement Units		
Lesson 20.1 Identify Metric Measurement Benchmarks	☐ Know relative sizes of measurement units within one system of units including km, m, cm; kg, g; lb, oz.; l, ml; hr, min, sec. Within a single system of measurement, express measurements in a larger unit in terms of a smaller unit. Record measurement equivalents in a two-column table.	1 day
Lesson 20.2 Compare Metric Units of Length	☐ Know relative sizes of measurement units within one system of units including km, m, cm; kg, g; lb, oz.; l, ml; hr, min, sec. Within a single system of measurement, express measurements in a larger unit in terms of a smaller unit. Record measurement equivalents in a two-column table.	1 day
Lesson 20.3 Compare Metric Units of Mass and Liquid Volume	☐ Know relative sizes of measurement units within one system of units including km, m, cm; kg, g; lb, oz.; l, ml; hr, min, sec. Within a single system of measurement, express measurements in a larger unit in terms of a smaller unit. Record measurement equivalents in a two-column table.	1 day

Module continued on next page →

Pacing Guide

Lesson	Mathematics Standards, Grade 4	Pacing
Module 20: Relative Sizes of Metric Measurement Units		
Lesson 20.4 Solve Problems Using Measurements	☐ Use the four operations to solve word problems involving distances, intervals of time, liquid volumes, masses of objects, and money, including problems involving simple fractions or decimals, and problems that require expressing measurements given in a larger unit in terms of a smaller unit. Represent measurement quantities using diagrams such as number line diagrams that feature a measurement scale.	1 day
Module 21: Solve Problems with Time and Measurement		
Lesson 21.1 Compare Units of Time	☐ Know relative sizes of measurement units within one system of units including km, m, cm; kg, g; lb, oz.; l, ml; hr, min, sec. Within a single system of measurement, express measurements in a larger unit in terms of a smaller unit. Record measurement equivalents in a two-column table.	1 day
Lesson 21.2 Solve Problems Involving Elapsed Time	☐ Use the four operations to solve word problems involving distances, intervals of time, liquid volumes, masses of objects, and money, including problems involving simple fractions or decimals, and problems that require expressing measurements given in a larger unit in terms of a smaller unit. Represent measurement quantities using diagrams such as number line diagrams that feature a measurement scale.	1 day
Lesson 21.3 Solve Problems Involving Start Time and End Time	☐ Use the four operations to solve word problems involving distances, intervals of time, liquid volumes, masses of objects, and money, including problems involving simple fractions or decimals, and problems that require expressing measurements given in a larger unit in terms of a smaller unit. Represent measurement quantities using diagrams such as number line diagrams that feature a measurement scale.	1 day
Lesson 21.4 Practice with Mixed Measure	☐ Use the four operations to solve word problems involving distances, intervals of time, liquid volumes, masses of objects, and money, including problems involving simple fractions or decimals, and problems that require expressing measurements given in a larger unit in terms of a smaller unit. Represent measurement quantities using diagrams such as number line diagrams that feature a measurement scale.	1 day

End-of-Year Options

Getting Ready Lessons

A variety of end-of-year options are available for teachers who aim to complete core instruction before a high-stakes assessment is administered. Utilizing standards reports or the recommendations tool, you can find and review content that students did not master or retain. Or, you can use the Getting Ready lessons. These lessons present on-grade-level content that is essential for setting a foundation for success with next year's content.

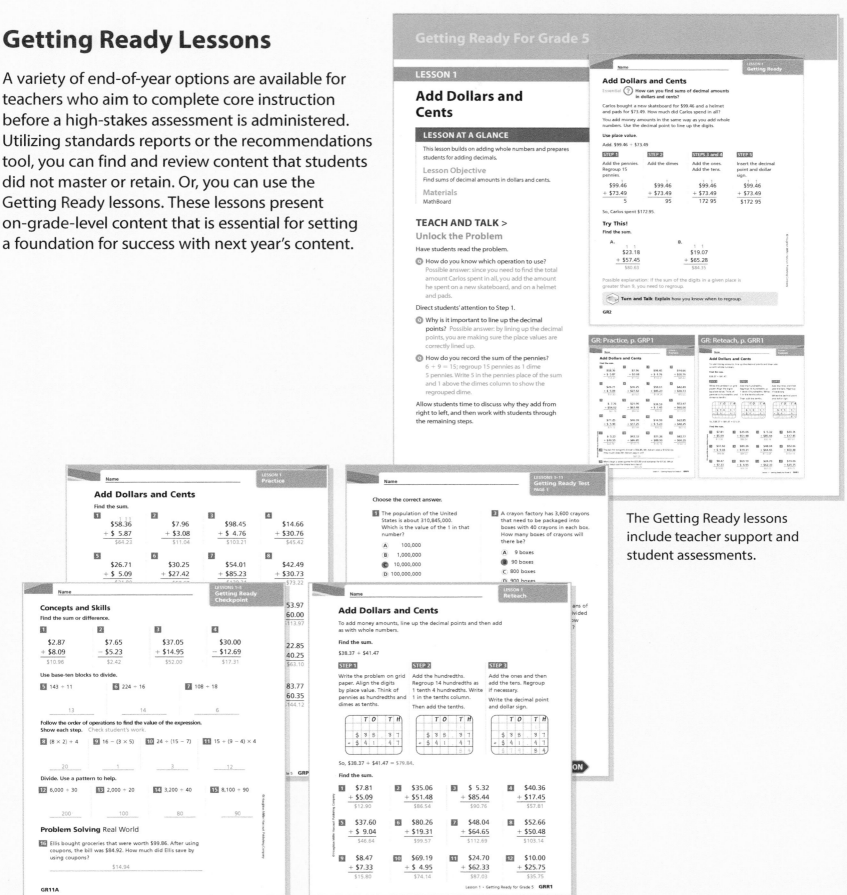

The Getting Ready lessons include teacher support and student assessments.

Teacher Notes

Notes & Reflections

Corlations

ONLINE

Search by state standard for standard-specific resources on Ed, Your Friend in Learning.

Standards and Mathematical Practices and Processes

Standards	Student Edition Lessons
Domain **OPERATIONS AND ALGEBRAIC THINKING**	
Cluster: **Use the four operations with whole numbers to solve problems.**	
Interpret a multiplication equation as a comparison, e.g., interpret $35 = 5 \times 7$ as a statement that 35 is 5 times as many as 7 and 7 times as many as 5. Represent verbal statements of multiplicative comparisons as multiplication equations.	3.1
Multiply or divide to solve word problems involving multiplicative comparison, e.g., by using drawings and equations with a symbol for the unknown number to represent the problem, distinguishing multiplicative comparison from additive comparison.	3.1, 3.2, 3.3, 3.4, 3.5
Solve multistep word problems posed with whole numbers and having whole-number answers using the four operations, including problems in which remainders must be interpreted. Represent these problems using equations with a letter standing for the unknown quantity. Assess the reasonableness of answers using mental computation and estimation strategies including rounding.	3.5, 5.7, 6.3, 7.4, 8.7
Cluster: **Gain familiarity with factors and multiples.**	
Find all factor pairs for a whole number in the range 1–100. Recognize that a whole number is a multiple of each of its factors. Determine whether a given whole number in the range 1–100 is a multiple of a given one-digit number. Determine whether a given whole number in the range 1–100 is prime or composite.	10.1, 10.2, 10.3, 10.4
Cluster: **Generate and analyze patterns.**	
Generate a number or shape pattern that follows a given rule. Identify apparent features of the pattern that were not explicit in the rule itself.	10.5, 18.3
Domain **NUMBER AND OPERATIONS IN BASE TEN**	
Cluster: **Generalize place value understanding for multi-digit whole numbers.**	
Recognize that in a multi-digit whole number, a digit in one place represents ten times what it represents in the place to its right.	1.1, 1.3
Read and write multi-digit whole numbers using base-ten numerals, number names, and expanded form. Compare two multi-digit numbers based on meanings of the digits in each place, using $>$, $=$, and $<$ symbols to record the results of comparisons.	1.2, 1.4
Use place value understanding to round multi-digit whole numbers to any place.	1.5, 4.3, 8.2
Cluster: **Use place value understanding and properties of operations to perform multi-digit arithmetic.**	
Fluently add and subtract multi-digit whole numbers using the standard algorithm.	2.1, 2.2, 2.3
Multiply a whole number of up to four digits by a one-digit whole number, and multiply two two-digit numbers, using strategies based on place value and the properties of operations. Illustrate and explain the calculation by using equations, rectangular arrays, and/or area models.	4.1, 4.3, 4.5, 5.1, 5.2, 5.3, 5.4, 5.5, 5.6, 8.1, 8.3, 8.4, 8.5, 8.6

Correlations

Standards	Student Edition Lessons
Find whole-number quotients and remainders with up to four-digit dividends and one-digit divisors, using strategies based on place value, the properties of operations, and/or the relationship between multiplication and division. Illustrate and explain the calculation by using equations, rectangular arrays, and/or area models.	4.2, 4.4, 4.5, 6.1, 6.2, 6.3, 6.4, 6.5, 6.6, 7.1, 7.2, 7.3

Domain NUMBER AND OPERATIONS—FRACTIONS	
Cluster: Extend understanding of fraction equivalence and ordering.	
Explain why a fraction a/b is equivalent to a fraction $(n \times a)/(n \times b)$ by using visual fraction models, with attention to how the number and size of the parts differ even though the two fractions themselves are the same size. Use this principle to recognize and generate equivalent fractions.	11.3, 11.4, 11.5
Compare two fractions with different numerators and different denominators, e.g., by creating common denominators or numerators, or by comparing to a benchmark fraction such as 1/2. Recognize that comparisons are valid only when the two fractions refer to the same whole. Record the results of comparisons with symbols >, =, or <, and justify the conclusions, e.g., by using a visual fraction model.	11.1, 11.2, 11.6, 11.7

Cluster: Build fractions from unit fractions by applying and extending previous understandings of operations on whole numbers.	
Understand a fraction a/b with $a > 1$ as a sum of fractions $1/b$.	
• Understand addition and subtraction of fractions as joining and separating parts referring to the same whole.	14.2, 14.4
• Decompose a fraction into a sum of fractions with the same denominator in more than one way, recording each decomposition by an equation. Justify decompositions, e.g., by using a visual fraction model.	14.1, 15.2
• Add and subtract mixed numbers with like denominators, e.g., by replacing each mixed number with an equivalent fraction, and/or by using properties of operations and the relationship between addition and subtraction.	15.3, 15.4, 15.5
• Solve word problems involving addition and subtraction of fractions referring to the same whole and having like denominators, e.g., by using visual fraction models and equations to represent the problem.	14.3, 14.5, 15.1, 15.6
Apply and extend previous understandings of multiplication to multiply a fraction by a whole number.	
• Understand a fraction a/b as a multiple of $1/b$.	16.1
• Understand a multiple of a/b as a multiple of $1/b$, and use this understanding to multiply a fraction by a whole number.	16.2, 16.3
• Solve word problems involving multiplication of a fraction by a whole number, e.g., by using visual fraction models and equations to represent the problem.	16.2, 16.3, 16.4

Cluster: Understand decimal notation for fractions, and compare decimal fractions.	
Express a fraction with denominator 10 as an equivalent fraction with denominator 100, and use this technique to add two fractions with respective denominators 10 and 100.	12.3, 14.6
Use decimal notation for fractions with denominators 10 or 100.	12.1, 12.2, 12.3, 12.5

Standards	Student Edition Lessons
Compare two decimals to hundredths by reasoning about their size. Recognize that comparisons are valid only when the two decimals refer to the same whole. Record the results of comparisons with the symbols $>$, $=$, or $<$, and justify the conclusions, e.g., by using a visual model.	12.4

Domain   MEASUREMENT AND DATA

Cluster: Solve problems involving measurement and conversion of measurements from a larger unit to a smaller unit.

Know relative sizes of measurement units within one system of units including km, m, cm; kg, g; lb, oz.; l, ml; hr, min, sec. Within a single system of measurement, express measurements in a larger unit in terms of a smaller unit. Record measurement equivalents in a two-column table.	19.1, 19.2, 19.3, 19.4, 20.1, 20.2, 20.3, 21.1
Use the four operations to solve word problems involving distances, intervals of time, liquid volumes, masses of objects, and money, including problems involving simple fractions or decimals, and problems that require expressing measurements given in a larger unit in terms of a smaller unit. Represent measurement quantities using diagrams such as number line diagrams that feature a measurement scale.	12.6, 19.5, 20.4, 21.2, 21.3, 21.4
Apply the area and perimeter formulas for rectangles in real world and mathematical problems.	2.4, 9.1, 9.2, 9.3, 9.4

Cluster: Represent and interpret data.

Make a line plot to display a data set of measurements in fractions of a unit (1/2, 1/4, 1/8). Solve problems involving addition and subtraction of fractions by using information presented in line plots.	19.5

Cluster: Geometric measurement: understand concepts of angle and measure angles.

Recognize angles as geometric shapes that are formed wherever two rays share a common endpoint, and understand concepts of angle measurement:	
• An angle is measured with reference to a circle with its center at the common endpoint of the rays, by considering the fraction of the circular arc between the points where the two rays intersect the circle. An angle that turns through 1/360 of a circle is called a "one-degree angle," and can be used to measure angles.	13.2, 13.3, 13.4
• An angle that turns through n one-degree angles is said to have an angle measure of n degrees.	13.4
Measure angles in whole-number degrees using a protractor. Sketch angles of specified measure.	13.5, 17.5
Recognize angle measure as additive. When an angle is decomposed into non-overlapping parts, the angle measure of the whole is the sum of the angle measures of the parts. Solve addition and subtraction problems to find unknown angles on a diagram in real world and mathematical problems, e.g., by using an equation with a symbol for the unknown angle measure.	13.6, 13.7

Domain   GEOMETRY

Cluster: Draw and identify lines and angles, and classify shapes by properties of their lines and angles.

Draw points, lines, line segments, rays, angles (right, acute, obtuse), and perpendicular and parallel lines. Identify these in two-dimensional figures.	13.1, 13.5, 17.1, 17.2, 17.3, 17.4, 17.5
Classify two-dimensional figures based on the presence or absence of parallel or perpendicular lines, or the presence or absence of angles of a specified size. Recognize right triangles as a category, and identify right triangles.	17.2, 17.3, 17.4
Recognize a line of symmetry for a two-dimensional figure as a line across the figure such that the figure can be folded along the line into matching parts. Identify line-symmetric figures and draw lines of symmetry.	18.1, 18.2

Correlations

Mathematical Practices and Processes	Student Edition Lessons
Into Math covers all Mathematical Practice and Process standards as an integral part of instruction and practice. For a summary of how the program features address each Mathematical Practice and Process standard see PG18–PG19. These pages include probing *Questions to Ask* that support each Mathematical Practice and Process standard.	
Make sense of problems and persevere in solving them. Mathematically proficient students start by explaining to themselves the meaning of a problem and looking for entry points to its solution. They analyze givens, constraints, relationships, and goals. They make conjectures about the form and meaning of the solution and plan a solution pathway rather than simply jumping into a solution attempt. They consider analogous problems, and try special cases and simpler forms of the original problem in order to gain insight into its solution. They monitor and evaluate their progress and change course if necessary. Older students might, depending on the context of the problem, transform algebraic expressions or change the viewing window on their graphing calculator to get the information they need. Mathematically proficient students can explain correspondences between equations, verbal descriptions, tables, and graphs or draw diagrams of important features and relationships, graph data, and search for regularity or trends. Younger students might rely on using concrete objects or pictures to help conceptualize and solve a problem. Mathematically proficient students check their answers to problems using a different method, and they continually ask themselves, "Does this make sense?" They can understand the approaches of others to solving complex problems and identify correspondences between different approaches.	In every lesson. Some examples include 1.5, 2.1, 3.2, 4.4, 5.7, 6.3, 7.2, 8.1, 9.2, 10.5, 11.2, 12.6, 13.4, 14.2, 15.4, 16.2, 17.1, 18.2, 19.3, 20.4, 21.1
Reason abstractly and quantitatively. Mathematically proficient students make sense of quantities and their relationships in problem situations. They bring two complementary abilities to bear on problems involving quantitative relationships: the ability to *decontextualize*—to abstract a given situation and represent it symbolically and manipulate the representing symbols as if they have a life of their own, without necessarily attending to their referents—and the ability to *contextualize*, to pause as needed during the manipulation process in order to probe into the referents for the symbols involved. Quantitative reasoning entails habits of creating a coherent representation of the problem at hand; considering the units involved; attending to the meaning of quantities, not just how to compute them; and knowing and flexibly using different properties of operations and objects.	1.4, 1.5, 2.1, 2.2, 4.1, 4.3, 4.4, 4.5, 5.1, 5.2, 5.3, 5.4, 5.5, 5.6, 5.7, 6.1, 6.2, 6.3, 6.4, 6.5, 7.1, 7.3, 7.4, 8.1, 8.2, 8.3, 8.5, 8.6, 8.7, 9.2, 10.2, 11.5, 11.6, 12.1, 12.2, 13.2, 13.3, 13.4, 14.5, 14.6, 15.3, 15.5, 16.1, 16.3, 16.4, 17.2, 17.5, 18.1, 19.1, 19.2, 20.1, 20.2
Construct viable arguments and critique the reasoning of others. Mathematically proficient students understand and use stated assumptions, definitions, and previously established results in constructing arguments. They make conjectures and build a logical progression of statements to explore the truth of their conjectures. They are able to analyze situations by breaking them into cases, and can recognize and use counterexamples. They justify their conclusions, communicate them to others, and respond to the arguments of others. They reason inductively about data, making plausible arguments that take into account the context from which the data arose. Mathematically proficient students are also able to compare the effectiveness of two plausible arguments, distinguish correct logic or reasoning from that which is flawed, and—if there is a flaw in an argument—explain what is. Elementary students can construct arguments using concrete referents such as objects, drawings, diagrams, and actions. Such arguments can make sense and be correct, even though they are not generalized or made formal until later grades. Later, students learn to determine domains to which an argument applies. Students at all grades can listen or read the arguments of others, decide whether they make sense, and ask useful questions to clarify or improve the arguments.	4.3, 7.2, 7.3, 7.4, 8.6, 10.1, 11.5, 12.3, 12.6, 14.2, 16.4, 19.1, 19.4, 21.1, 21.2, 21.3

Mathematical Practices and Processes	Student Edition Lessons
Model with mathematics. Mathematically proficient students can apply the mathematics they know to solve problems arising in everyday life, society, and the workplace. In early grades, this might be as simple as writing an addition equation to describe a situation. In middle grades, a student might apply proportional reasoning to plan a school event or analyze a problem in the community. By high school, a student might use geometry to solve a design problem or use a function to describe how one quantity of interest depends on another. Mathematically proficient students who can apply what they know are comfortable making assumptions and approximations to simplify a complicated situation, realizing that these may need revision later. They are able to identify important quantities in a practical situation and map their relationships using such tools as diagrams, two-way tables, graphs, flowcharts and formulas. They can analyze those relationships mathematically to draw conclusions. They routinely interpret their mathematical results in the context of the situation and reflect on whether the results make sense, possibly improving the model if it has not served its purpose.	2.3, 2.4, 3.1, 3.2, 3.3, 3.4, 3.5, 5.2, 5.4, 5.7, 6.1, 6.5, 7.4, 8.3, 8.7, 12.6, 13.2, 13.6, 13.7, 14.1, 14.2, 14.3, 14.6, 15.1, 15.2, 15.3, 15.4, 15.6, 16.2, 19.3, 19.4, 19.5, 20.1, 20.4, 21.2, 21.3
Use appropriate tools strategically. Mathematically proficient students consider the available tools when solving a mathematical problem. These tools might include pencil and paper, concrete models, a ruler, a protractor, a calculator, a spreadsheet, a computer algebra system, a statistical package, or dynamic geometry software. Proficient students are sufficiently familiar with tools appropriate for their grade or course to make sound decisions about when each of these tools might be helpful, recognizing both the insight to be gained and their limitations. For example, mathematically proficient high school students analyze graphs of functions and solutions generated using a graphing calculator. They detect possible errors by strategically using estimation and other mathematical knowledge. When making mathematical models, they know that technology can enable them to visualize the results of varying assumptions, explore consequences, and compare predictions with data. Mathematically proficient students at various grade levels are able to identify relevant external mathematical resources, such as digital content located on a website, and use them to pose or solve problems. They are able to use technological tools to explore and deepen their understanding of concepts.	In every Spark Your Learning, Module Review, and the following lessons: 1.1, 1.4, 1.5, 2.3, 3.5, 4.3, 6.2, 6.3, 6.4, 7.1, 7.2, 9.3, 9.4, 10.1, 10.2, 10.5, 11.1, 11.2, 11.3, 12.1, 13.4, 13.5, 13.6, 13.7, 14.4, 14.5, 15.1, 15.3, 17.1, 17.2, 17.3, 17.4, 17.5, 18.2, 20.1, 21.2, 21.3
Attend to precision. Mathematically proficient students try to communicate precisely to others. They try to use clear definitions in discussion with others and in their own reasoning. They state the meaning of the symbols they choose, including using the equal sign consistently and appropriately. They are careful about specifying units of measure, and labeling axes to clarify the correspondence with quantities in a problem. They calculate accurately and efficiently, express numerical answers with a degree of precision appropriate for the problem context. In the elementary grades, students give carefully formulated explanations to each other. By the time they reach high school they have learned to examine claims and make explicit use of definitions.	2.1, 4.4, 6.3, 6.5, 6.6, 9.1, 9.2, 11.7, 13.1, 17.1, 17.2, 17.3, 17.4, 17.5, 18.1, 18.3, 19.2, 19.3, 19.5, 20.2, 20.3, 20.4, 21.4

Correlations

Mathematical Practices and Processes	Student Edition Lessons
Look for and make use of structure. Mathematically proficient students look closely to discern a pattern or structure. Young students, for example, might notice that three and seven more is the same amount as seven and three more, or they may sort a collection of shapes according to how many sides the shapes have. Later, students will see 7×8 equals the well remembered $7 \times 5 + 7 \times 3$, in preparation for learning about the distributive property. In the expression $x^2 + 9x + 14$, older students can see the 14 as 2×7 and the 9 as $2 + 7$. They recognize the significance of an existing line in a geometric figure and can use the strategy of drawing an auxiliary line for solving problems. They also can step back for an overview and shift perspective. They can see complicated things, such as some algebraic expressions, as single objects or as being composed of several objects. For example, they can see $5 - 3(x - y)^2$ as 5 minus a positive number times a square and use that to realize that its value cannot be more than 5 for any real numbers x and y.	1.1, 1.2, 1.3, 2.1, 2.2, 2.4, 3.4, 4.1, 4.2, 4.5, 5.1, 5.3, 5.5, 5.6, 5.7, 6.1, 6.2, 6.4, 6.6, 7.2, 7.3, 8.1, 8.4, 8.5, 9.1, 9.3, 9.4, 10.2, 10.3, 10.4, 11.2, 11.4, 11.5, 12.3, 12.4, 14.1, 15.4, 15.5, 16.1, 16.2, 16.3, 18.2, 18.3, 19.3, 19.4, 20.3, 21.4
Look for and express regularity in repeated reasoning. Mathematically proficient students notice if calculations are repeated, and look both for general methods and for shortcuts. Upper elementary students might notice when dividing 25 by 11 that they are repeating the same calculations over and over again, and conclude they have a repeating decimal. By paying attention to the calculation of slope as they repeatedly check whether points are on the line through $(1, 2)$ with slope 3, middle school students might abstract the equation $(y - 2)/(x - 1) = 3$. Noticing the regularity in the way terms cancel when expanding $(x - 1)(x + 1)$, $(x - 1)(x^2 + x + 1)$, and $(x - 1)(x^3 + x^2 + x + 1)$ might lead them to the general formula for the sum of a geometric series. As they work to solve a problem, mathematically proficient students maintain oversight of the process, while attending to the details. They continually evaluate the reasonableness of their intermediate results.	1.2, 1.3, 1.5, 2.2, 4.2, 6.6, 8.4, 8.5, 8.6, 10.3, 10.4, 10.5, 11.4, 11.6, 11.7, 12.2, 12.4, 12.5, 15.2, 21.1

Notes & Reflections

Jennifer Lempp
Educational Consultant
Alexandria, Virginia

Problem Solving Structures

Introducing Students to a Variety of Structures

We all want the same for students, to be independent problem solvers and thinkers. The types of problems we provide and the way we present them can ultimately support or hinder students. Most students are not given the opportunity to truly reason with a variety of word problems. Rather, students are often given problems that closely resemble the first problem below. The problem contains two numbers that you act upon in some way. The answer to the problem is unknown. However, students should be exposed to problems that have the start or the change unknown as well.

Let's consider these two problems:

- Anna had 7 books checked out from the library. She returned 4 books. How many books does Anna still have to return?
- Anna read 7 books, and Jon read 4 books. How many more books did Anna read than Jon?

Both problems could be solved using the equation $7 - 4 =$ _____. However, as students begin to translate story problems, the context of these problems varies quite a bit. The first can be considered a "take away" problem and the second a "compare" problem. If we always refer to subtraction as "take away," then we are removing the true context of the mathematics that exists in the world around us.

Various problem structures exist for addition, subtraction, multiplication, and division. Students do not need to be able to identify these structures, but it's important that teachers know the variety of structures and expose students to them.

Don't Steal the Struggle

The context within word problems helps to support mathematical thinking. Many teachers may shy away from problem solving, seeing it as more complex than a "numbers only" problem. However, students do not need to master the skill of computation in order to solve problems. In fact, the context used in problem solving can often help students make sense of the numbers, making the students more successful.

When introducing a word problem, don't be tempted to model a similar problem first and then give students a problem that simply contains different numbers. This results in stealing the students' struggle and takes away the opportunity for thinking and reasoning. Moreover, students should be encouraged to solve problems using whatever strategy or technique that they wish. It is also important to note that teachers should not teach "key words" to students as a system of support for students. Students are often told that words like "altogether" and "in all" are supposed to signal to students that they are to add, while words like "how many more" mean they are to subtract. However, key words can lead students to choose the wrong operation. Teaching key words takes away the thinking and sends the message that there is no reasoning necessary – that math is just about numbers and is not even a part of our real life. What is most important is their reasoning and why they chose to solve it in the way they did. The strategies used by students provide teachers with a great deal of information about where a student is and where to go next with him or her.

Addition and Subtraction Problem Situations – Add To/Take From

Add To/Take From problems have three components. There is an initial quantity – the **start**. The **change** is the action upon that initial quantity. The outcome of the action upon the initial quantity is the **result**.

	RESULT UNKNOWN	*INTO MATH* EXAMPLES
ADD TO	A problem in which the **start** and **change** (what is *added to* the start) are given in the problem. The **result** of the change is not known and is what the students determine.	**7** (MP) **Model with Mathematics** Keisha pours $\frac{9}{10}$ liter of orange juice into a jug. Then she pours $\frac{8}{100}$ liter of lemon juice into the jug. How much juice is in the jug? $\frac{9}{10} + \frac{8}{100} = \blacksquare$ Example from Lesson 14.6, Problem 7 Additional Lessons 12.6, 14.5, 15.1
TAKE FROM	A problem in which the **start** and **change** (what is *taken from* the start) are given in the problem. The **result** of the change is not known and is what the students determine.	**1** Michael had $\frac{3}{4}$ cup of flour. He used $\frac{2}{4}$ cup in a recipe. How much flour does Michael have now? Draw a fraction model to solve. $\frac{3}{4} - \frac{2}{4} = \blacksquare$ Example from Lesson 14.4, Problem 1 Additional Lessons 5.7, 12.6, 14.5, 15.1, 15.3, 15.6
	CHANGE UNKNOWN	*INTO MATH* EXAMPLES
ADD TO	A problem in which the **start** and **result** (the outcome of the performing action) are given in the problem. The **change** (what is added to the start) is not known and is what the students determine.	**5** (MP) **Attend to Precision** Kyra has $1\frac{3}{8}$ pounds of clay. How much clay must she buy to have $2\frac{7}{8}$ pounds of clay to make a vase? $1\frac{3}{8} + \blacksquare = 2\frac{7}{8}$ Example from Lesson 15.3, Problem 5 Additional Lessons 5.7, 15.4, 21.2
TAKE FROM	A problem in which the **start** and **result** (the outcome of the performing action) are given in the problem. The **change** (what is taken from the start) is not known and is what the students determine.	**6** (MP) **Model with Mathematics** Oliver has a board that is $\frac{10}{12}$ foot long. After he cuts some off, he has $\frac{7}{12}$ foot left. How much did Oliver cut off? Model the problem with an equation. $\frac{10}{12} - \blacksquare = \frac{7}{12}$ Example from Lesson 14.5, Problem 6 Additional Lessons 13.7, 15.4

Problem Types

	START UNKNOWN	*INTO MATH* EXAMPLES
ADD TO	A problem in which the **change** (what is *added to* the start) and **result** (the outcome of the performing action) are given in the problem. The **start** is not known and is what the students determine.	**10** Mr. Tate wants to paint a house. He has some paint and buys another $5\frac{3}{6}$ gallons. He now has $14\frac{1}{6}$ gallons of paint. How much paint did Mr. Tate start with? $$\blacksquare + 5\frac{3}{6} = 14\frac{1}{6}$$ $$14\frac{1}{6} - 5\frac{3}{6} = \blacksquare$$ Example from Lesson 15.6, Problem 10
TAKE FROM	A problem in which the **change** (what is *taken from* the start) and **result** (the outcome of the performing action) are given in the problem. The **start** is not known and is what the students determine.	**3** (MP) **Reason** Brad has some water in a bucket. He pours $\frac{3}{10}$ liter of the water on some house plants. Now there is $\frac{4}{10}$ liter of water in the bucket. How many liters of water did Brad have in the bucket before watering the plants? $$\blacksquare - \frac{3}{10} = \frac{4}{10}$$ $$\frac{4}{10} + \frac{3}{10} = \blacksquare$$ Example from Lesson 15.1, Problem 3

Addition and Subtraction Problem Situations – Put Together/Take Apart

In a *Put Together/Take Apart* problem both quantities are already present. Unlike an *Add To/Take From* problem, these problems do not involve a change in the situation. The **total** is unknown or one or both of the **quantities** (or **groups**) are unknown.

	TOTAL UNKNOWN	INTO MATH EXAMPLES
PUT TOGETHER/ TAKE APART	A problem in which the **two groups/quantities** are known. The **total** is not known and is what the students determine.	**1** A company's buses make 480,000 trips. A second company's buses make 44,100 trips. How many trips do the two companies' buses make? $480,000 + 44,100 = \blacksquare$ Example from Lesson 2.1, Problem 1 Additional Lessons 13.6, 14.2, 14.3, 14.6, 15.1, 15.3, 15.6
	ADDEND UNKNOWN	**INTO MATH EXAMPLES**
	A problem in which **one of the two groups/quantities** is known and the **total** is also known. The **other group/quantity** is not known and is what the students determine.	**5** **Financial Literacy** Financial planners suggest that $\frac{8}{10}$ of your income should be used for spending. The rest should go into savings. If you spend $\frac{5}{10}$ of your income to pay bills, how much of your income could you spend on other purchases? $\frac{5}{10} + \blacksquare = \frac{8}{10}$ $\frac{8}{10} - \frac{5}{10} = \blacksquare$ Example from Lesson 14.4, Problem 5 Additional Lesson 13.6
	BOTH ADDENDS UNKNOWN	**INTO MATH EXAMPLES**
	A problem in which the **total** is known. The **two groups/ quantities** are not known and are what the students determine.	**Build Understanding, Task 2** Tony and his family drove $\frac{7}{12}$ of the distance across Michigan on Saturday. What are three ways they could break up the drive into 2 parts so they could stop and walk their dog? $\frac{7}{12} = \blacksquare + \blacktriangle$ Example from Lesson 14.1, Build Understanding, Task 2 Additional Lessons 14.6, 15.1

Problem Types

Addition and Subtraction Problem Situations – Compare

Compare problems involve two separate quantities. In these problems, students seek to determine the larger quantity, the smaller quantity, or the difference between the two quantities.

	DIFFERENCE UNKNOWN	INTO MATH EXAMPLES
COMPARE	Two known quantities are compared to find how many more there are of the **larger quantity**.	**1** A scientific database lists 7,858 species of amphibians, and another database lists 5,513 species of mammals. How many more amphibian species than mammal species are listed? $$5{,}513 + \blacksquare = 7{,}858$$ $$7{,}858 - 5{,}513 = \blacksquare$$ Example from Lesson 2.2, Problem 1 Additional Lessons 3.4, 14.5, 15.3, 15.6
	Two known quantities are compared to find how many fewer there are of the **smaller quantity**.	**2** Pablo spends $3\frac{1}{6}$ hours painting, and Miguel spends $1\frac{5}{6}$ hours painting. How many fewer hours does Miguel spend painting than Pablo? Show your work. $$1\frac{5}{6} + \blacksquare = 3\frac{1}{6}$$ $$3\frac{1}{6} - 1\frac{5}{6} = \blacksquare$$ Example from Lesson 15.4, Problem 2 Additional Lessons 2.3, 3.4

	BIGGER UNKNOWN	INTO MATH EXAMPLES
	The **smaller quantity** is known along with the **difference** between the smaller quantity and the unknown **greater quantity**. The problem is stated so that the unknown quantity is described as 'greater than' the known quantity.	**1** A park had 4,307 visitors on Thursday and 1,614 more visitors on Friday than on Thursday. How many visitors did the park have on Friday? $$1{,}614 + 4{,}307 = \blacksquare$$ $$4{,}307 + 1{,}614 = \blacksquare$$ Example from Lesson 2.3, Problem 1 Additional Lessons 3.2, 3.4, 14.3, 15.6, 21.4
	The **smaller quantity** is known along with the **difference** between the smaller quantity and the unknown **greater quantity**. The problem is stated so that the known quantity is described as 'less than' or 'fewer than' the unknown quantity.	

	SMALLER UNKNOWN	*INTO MATH* EXAMPLES
COMPARE	The **larger quantity** is known along with the **difference** between the larger quantity and the unknown **smaller quantity**. The problem is stated so that the known quantity is described as 'more than' the unknown quantity.	**5** Amir wants to put a fence around a garden and another around a fruit tree. He needs $6\frac{3}{8}$ yards to fence in the garden. He needs $1\frac{4}{8}$ yards more fencing for the garden than for the fruit tree. How much fencing does he need for the fruit tree? $$\blacksquare + 1\frac{4}{8} = 6\frac{3}{8}$$ $$6\frac{3}{8} - 1\frac{4}{8} = \blacksquare$$ Example from Lesson 15.6, Problem 5 Additional Lesson 3.4
	The **larger quantity** is known along with the **difference** between the larger quantity and the unknown **smaller quantity**. The problem is stated so that the unknown quantity is described as 'fewer/less than' the known quantity.	**1** Tina donates 3 fewer cans of corn than green beans. She donates 15 cans of green beans. How many cans of corn does Tina donate? $$15 - 3 = \blacksquare$$ $$\blacksquare + 3 = 15$$ Example from Lesson 3.4, Problem 1 Additional Lessons 3.4, 15.6, 21.4

Problem Types

Multiplication and Division Problem Situations – Equal Groups

Equal Groups problems have the quantities organized into groups of the same size or amount. In these problems, the first factor is the number of groups, the second factor is the number of objects in each group or the group size, and the product is the total number of objects.

	UNKNOWN PRODUCT	INTO MATH EXAMPLES
EQUAL GROUPS	A problem in which the **number of groups** and the **number of objects** in each group are given. The total number of objects, the **product**, is not known and is what the students determine.	**2** Each box has 8 prizes. How many prizes are in 5,000 boxes? $5{,}000 \times 8 = \blacksquare$ Example from Lesson 4.1, Problem 2 Additional Lessons 4.5, 5.3, 5.4, 5.5, 5.6, 8.1, 8.4, 8.5, 8.6, 15.3, 16.1, 16.4

	GROUP SIZE UNKNOWN	INTO MATH EXAMPLES
EQUAL GROUPS	A problem in which the **number of groups** and the **product** are given. The **number of objects** in each group is not known and is what the students determine.	**2** Ari has 2,000 marbles. He puts the same number of marbles in each of 5 bags. How many marbles are in each bag? $5 \times \blacksquare = 2{,}000$ $2{,}000 \div 5 = \blacksquare$ Example from Lesson 4.2, Problem 2 Additional Lessons 4.5, 6.1, 6.3, 6.5, 6.6. 7.1, 7.2, 7.3

	NUMBER OF GROUPS UNKNOWN	INTO MATH EXAMPLES
EQUAL GROUPS	A problem in which the **number of objects** in each group and the **product** are given. The **number of groups** is not known and is what the students determine.	**2** A basketball player makes 93 points from 3-point shots. How many 3-point shots does the player make? $\blacksquare \times 3 = 93$ $93 \div 3 = \blacksquare$ Example from Lesson 6.1, Problem 2 Additional Lessons 6.2, 6.3, 6.4, 6.5, 10.2, 15.6

Multiplication and Division Problem Situations – Array/Area

Problems that use an *array* have the set of objects organized into rows with the same number of objects in each row. In these problems the **number of rows** is the number of groups (the first factor), the group size or **number of objects** in each row (the second factor), and the total number of objects is the **product.** This can also be described as rows and columns, which is often more difficult for students.

Problems that use an *area* model represent multiplication with a rectangle, with the **length** and **width** representing the factors. Arrays and area are related in that area is like an array where there is no space between the objects in the rows.

	UNKNOWN PRODUCT	INTO MATH EXAMPLES
ARRAYS/AREA	*Arrays* A problem in which the **number of rows** and the **number of objects** in each row are given. The total number of objects, the **product,** is not known and is what the students determine.	**Spark Your Learning** A school scramble band gets into formation for a parade. There are 9 rows of 18 band members. How can you make a visual model to show the number of band members that are in the scramble band? $9 \times 18 = \blacksquare$ Example from Lesson 5.2, Spark Your Learning
	Area A problem in which the **length** and the **width** are given. The **product** is not known and is what the students determine.	1 Mr. Nielsen is going to buy sod for a portion of his yard, but first, he must know the area of the surface that he wants to cover. What is the area? 25 feet 18 feet — Mr. Nielsen's yard $18 \times 25 = \blacksquare$ Example from Lesson 9.1, Problem 1 Additional Lesson 9.4

Problem Types

ARRAYS/AREA	GROUP SIZE UNKNOWN	*INTO MATH* EXAMPLES
	Arrays A problem in which the **number of rows** and the **product** are given. The **number of objects** in each row is not known and is what the students determine.	**2** A memory game requires 55 cards. Beth places the cards in 5 equal rows. How many cards are in each row? $5 \times \blacksquare = 55$ Example from Lesson 6.1, Build Understanding, Task 2 Additional Lessons 7.2, 7.3, 10.2
	Area A problem in which the **length** and the **product** are given. The **width** is not known and is what the students determine.	**4** Jackie is marking off a section of a yard to practice field hockey. The area of the section is 56 square meters. The length is 8 meters. What is the width of the section? $56 = 8 \times \blacksquare$ Example from Lesson 9.3, Problem 4 Additional Lesson 6.5
	NUMBER OF GROUPS UNKNOWN	*INTO MATH* EXAMPLES
	Array A problem in which the **number of objects** in each row and the **product** are given. The **number of rows** is not known and is what the students determine.	**Build Understanding, Task 1** An airplane has 165 seats. There are 5 seats in each row. How many rows of seats are there? $165 \div 5 = \blacksquare$ $\blacksquare \times 5 = 165$ Example from Lesson 6.6, Build Understanding, Task 1
	Area A problem in which the **width** and the **product** are given. The **length** is not known and is what the students determine.	**1** Elise is painting a stage set that has an area of 48 square feet. The width of the set is 6 feet. What is the length? $48 \div 6 = \blacksquare$ $\blacksquare \times 6 = 48$ Example from Lesson 9.3, Problem 1

Multiplication and Division Problem Situations – Compare

Compare problems involve the relationships between a **larger quantity** and a **smaller quantity**. In these problems, one quantity is described as a **multiple** of the other quantity. The relationship between the two quantities is described as one quantity being a certain number of times as great as the other.

	SITUATIONS IN WHICH THE MULTIPLIER IS GREATER THAN 1	
	LARGER UNKNOWN	*INTO MATH* **EXAMPLES**
Compare	The **smaller quantity** is known along with the **multiplier**. The problem is stated in terms of the **larger quantity** (the unknown) being "*x* times as much" as the known smaller quantity (where *x* is the multiplier).	**2** (MP) **Use Tools** Frank and Shari play basketball. Shari makes 2 baskets. Frank makes 4 times as many baskets as Shari. Complete the bar model and write an equation to find how many baskets Frank makes. $4 \times 2 = \blacksquare$ Example from Lesson 3.1, Problem 2 Additional Lessons 3.2, 3.4
	SMALLER UNKNOWN	*INTO MATH* **EXAMPLES**
	The **larger quantity** is known. The problem is stated in terms of the known larger quantity being a given number of times (the **multiplier**) as much as the **smaller quantity** (the unknown).	**2** The students in the cooking club bake 12 blueberry muffins. They bake twice as many blueberry muffins as corn muffins. How many corn muffins do the students bake? $2 \times \blacksquare = 12$ $12 \div 2 = \blacksquare$ Example from Lesson 3.3, Problem 2 Additional Lesson 3.4
	MULTIPLIER UNKNOWN	*INTO MATH* **EXAMPLES**
	The **larger quantity** and the **smaller quantity** are known. The problem is stated in terms of the known larger quantity being "how many times" as much as the known smaller quantity.	**1** Leslie collects 24 aluminum cans and 8 glass bottles for the recycling club. How many times as many cans as bottles does Leslie collect? $\blacksquare \times 8 = 24$ $24 \div 8 = \blacksquare$ Example from Lesson 3.3, Problem 1 Additional Lesson 3.4

Differentiated Support Using *Do The Math*

Do The Math can be implemented with *Into Math* core instruction during the Differentiated Options block or as a separate instruction block. Depending on student level, *Do The Math* instruction can be provided as Tier 1, 2, or 3 support.

Do The Math as Tier 1 Support *Do The Math* Addition & Subtraction, Multiplication, Division, and Fractions modules provide Tier 1 supports for the following **Grade 4** skills as shown in the tables below.

Grade 4 Skills	Addition & Subtraction Modules		
	A	**B**	**C**
Read and write multi-digit whole numbers using expanded form.			X
Fluently add and subtract multi-digit whole numbers using the standard algorithm.			X
Multiply two two-digit numbers using place value and the properties of operations.			X
Compare two multi-digit numbers based on meanings of the digits in each place, using >, =, and < symbols to record the results of comparisons.			X

Grade 4 Skills	Multiplication Modules		
	A	**B**	**C**
Interpret a multiplication equation as a comparison.	X		
Represent verbal statements of multiplicative comparisons as multiplication equations.	X		
Find all factor pairs for a whole number in the range 1–100.		X	X
Recognize that a whole number is a multiple of each of its factors.		X	
Generate a number pattern that follows a given rule.		X	
Illustrate and explain the calculation of multiplication by using area models.		X	
Multiply a whole number of up to four digits by a one-digit whole number.			X
Assess the reasonableness of answers to multistep word problems using estimation.		X	X

Grade 4 Skills	Division Modules		
	A	**B**	**C**
Divide to solve word problems involving multiplicative comparison.	X	X	
Find whole-number quotients and remainders with up to 2-digit dividends and 1-digit divisors.	X	X	X
Illustrate and explain the calculation of whole-number quotients and remainders with up to four-digit dividends.	X	X	X

Grade 4 Skills	Fractions Modules		
	A	**B**	**C**
Record the results of fraction comparisons with symbols >, =, or <, and justify the conclusions.		X	X
Understand addition and subtraction of fractions as joining and separating parts.	X	X	X
Add mixed numbers with like denominators.	X		X
Compare two fractions with different numerators and denominators using a benchmark.	X		X
Recognize and generate equivalent fractions.		X	X
Recognize that fraction comparisons are valid when the two fractions refer to the same whole.		X	
Decompose a fraction into a sum of fractions with the same denominator (more than one way).			X

Do The Math as Tier 2 and Tier 3 Support The following *Do The Math* Addition & Subtraction, Multiplication, Division, and Fractions modules reinforce the Grade 3 skills, and may be used to provide Tier 2 and Tier 3 supports in **Grade 4**.

Grade 3 Skills	Addition & Subtraction Modules		
	A	**B**	**C**
Fluently add within 1000 using strategies and algorithms.			X

Grade 3 Skills	Multiplication Modules		
	A	**B**	**C**
Interpret products of whole numbers.	X	X	
Use multiplication within 100 to solve word problems.	X	X	X
Determine the unknown whole number in a multiplication equation relating 3 whole numbers.	X	X	X
Identify arithmetic patterns (including patterns in the addition table or multiplication table).		X	
Find the area of a rectangle with whole-number side lengths.		X	
Represent whole-number products as rectangular areas in mathematical reasoning.		X	
Multiply one-digit whole numbers by multiples of 10 in the range 10–90 (e.g., 9×80, 5×60).		X	X
Explain arithmetic patterns using properties of operations.		X	
Apply properties of operations as strategies to multiply.			X

Grade 3 Skills	Division Modules		
	A	**B**	**C**
Interpret whole-number quotients of whole numbers.	X	X	
Use division within 100 to solve word problems.	X		
Determine the unknown whole number in a division equation relating three whole numbers.	X		
Apply properties of operations as strategies to divide.	X		
Understand division as an unknown-factor problem.		X	
Fluently divide within 100.		X	X

Differentiated Support Using *Do The Math*

Grade 3 Skills	Fractions Modules		
	A	**B**	**C**
Express whole numbers as fractions.	X		
Understand a fraction $\frac{1}{b}$ as the quantity formed by 1 part when a whole is partitioned into b equal parts.	X		
Recognize fractions that are equivalent to whole numbers.	X		
Explain why equivalent fractions are equivalent, e.g., by using a visual fraction model.	X		
Record the results of comparisons with the symbols $>$, $=$, or $<$, and justify the conclusions.	X	X	
Recognize simple equivalent fractions.	X		
Generate simple equivalent fractions.	X	X	
Understand a fraction $\frac{a}{b}$ as the quantity formed by a parts of size $\frac{1}{b}$.	X	X	
Understand two fractions as equivalent (equal) if they are the same size.	X		
Understand two fractions as equivalent (equal) if they are the same point on a number line.	X		
Compare two fractions with the same numerator by reasoning about their size.		X	
Compare two fractions with the same denominator by reasoning about their size.		X	
Express whole numbers as fractions.		X	

Manipulatives and Tools

Into Math provides opportunities for students to choose manipulatives and tools to help them make sense of mathematics and connect to mathematical representations. Giving students the opportunity to choose a manipulative or tool for a task provides a teacher insight into a student's understanding of connections they are making with prior learning.

The tables below will help you plan which manipulatives and tools to have available for students during lesson instruction.

● Manipulative Kit   ● Basic Manipulative Kit   ● Teacher Resource Masters

Module	Manipulatives and Tools by Lesson
Module 1: Place Value of Whole Numbers	● ● **base-ten blocks (ones, tens, hundreds, thousand)** Lessons 1.1, 1.3 ● **Number Lines (by tens and hundreds)** Lessons 1.4–1.5 ● **Place-Value Charts (to hundred thousands)** Lessons 1.2–1.5
Module 2: Addition and Subtraction of Whole Numbers	● ● **base-ten blocks (ones, tens, hundreds, thousand)** Lessons 2.1–2.2 ● **Place-Value Charts (to hundred thousands)** Lessons 2.1–2.3
Module 3: Interpret and Solve Problem Situations	● **Number Lines (by ones)** Lessons 3.1–3.2 ● **square tiles** Lessons 3.1–3.2 ● **two-color counters** Lessons 3.1–3.2
Module 4: Mental Math and Estimation Strategies	● ● **base-ten blocks (ones, hundreds)** Lessons 4.1–4.4 ● **Number Lines (by ones)** Lesson 4.2 ● **Number Lines (by tens and hundreds)** Lessons 4.1–4.4 ● **square tiles** Lessons 4.1–4.2 ● **two-color counters** Lessons 4.1–4.2
Module 5: Multiply by 1-Digit Numbers	● ● **base-ten blocks (ones, tens, hundreds, thousand)** Lessons 5.1–5.7 ● **centimeter ruler** Lesson 5.3 ● **Place-Value Charts (to thousands)** Lesson 5.6 ● **two-color counters** Lesson 5.1
Module 6: Understand Division by 1-Digit Numbers	● **0.5-Centimeter Grid Paper** Lesson 6.6 ● **1-Centimeter Grid Paper** Lessons 6.4 ● ● **base-ten blocks (ones, tens)** Lessons 6.1–6.3, 6.5–6.6 ● **Number Lines (by ones)** Lessons 6.5–6.6 ● **square tiles** Lessons 6.1–6.4 ● **two-color counters** Lessons 6.1–6.3, 6.5

Manipulatives and Tools

● Manipulative Kit ● Basic Manipulative Kit ● Teacher Resource Masters

Module	Manipulatives and Tools by Lesson
Module 7: Divide by 1-Digit Numbers	● ● **base-ten blocks (ones, tens, hundreds)** Lessons 7.1–7.2
Module 8: Multiply by 2-Digit Numbers	● **1-Centimeter Grid Paper** Lesson 8.1 ● ● **base-ten blocks (ones, tens)** Lesson 8.1
Module 9: Apply Multiplication to Area	● **inch ruler / centimeter ruler** Lesson 9.1 ● **square tiles** Lesson 9.1
Module 10: Algebraic Thinking: Number Theory	● **0.5-Centimeter Grid Paper** Lessons 10.1, 10.2, 10.4 ● **square tiles** Lessons 10.1–10.2
Module 11: Fraction Equivalence and Comparison	● ● **fraction circles** Lessons 11.1–11.3 ● ● **fraction strips** Lessons 11.1–11.3 ● **Number Lines (fractions)** Lessons 11.1–11.2
Module 12: Relate Fractions and Decimals	● **Decimal Models (hundredths)** Lesson 12.3 ● **Decimal Models (tenths)** Lessons 12.1, 12.3 ● **Number Lines (fractions)** Lesson 12.1 ● **Number Lines (fraction and decimal equivalence)** Lesson 12.3 ● **Number Lines (tenths and hundredths)** Lessons 12.1–12.2 ● **Place-Value Charts (decimals)** Lesson 12.3
Module 13: Use Fractions to Understand Angles	● ● **fraction circles** Lesson 13.3 ● **inch ruler / centimeter ruler** Lessons 13.1–13.2 ● **protractor** Lessons 13.5–13.6
Module 14: Understand Addition and Subtraction of Fractions with Like Denominators	● ● **fraction circles** Lessons 14.1–14.5 ● ● **fraction strips** Lessons 14.1–14.5 ● **Number Lines (fractions)** Lessons 14.3–14.5
Module 15: Add and Subtract Fractions and Mixed Numbers with Like Denominators	● ● **fraction circles** Lessons 15.1–15.4 ● ● **fraction strips** Lessons 15.1–15.4 ● **Number Lines (fraction equivalence 1)** Lessons 15.1–15.2, 15.4 ● **Number Lines (fraction equivalence 2)** Lessons 15.3–15.4
Module 16: Multiply Fractions by Whole Numbers	● ● **fraction circles** Lessons 16.1–16.3 ● ● **fraction strips** Lessons 16.1–16.3 ● **Number Lines (fraction equivalence 1)** Lesson 16.3 ● **Number Lines (fractions)** Lesson 16.1
Module 17: Two-Dimensional Figures	● **centimeter ruler** Lessons 17.1, 17.3 ● **protractor** Lessons 17.2, 17.5

Manipulatives and Tools

● Manipulative Kit ● Basic Manipulative Kit ● Teacher Resource Masters

Module	Manipulatives and Tools by Lesson
Module 18: Symmetry and Patterns	● **1-Centimeter Grid Paper** Lessons 18.1, 18.3 ● **Dot Paper (square)** Lesson 18.1 ● **pattern blocks** Lesson 18.3
Module 19: Relative Sizes of Customary Measurement Units	● **inch ruler** Lessons 19.1–19.2 ● **Number Lines (by ones)** Lessons 19.2–19.3 ● **spring scale** Lessons 19.1, 19.3 ● **square tiles** Lesson 19.2
Module 20: Relative Sizes of Metric Measurement Units	● ● **base-ten blocks (ones, tens, hundreds)** Lesson 20.2 ● **centimeter ruler** Lessons 20.1–20.2 ● **Number Lines (tenths and hundredths)** Lesson 20.2
Module 21: Solve Problems with Time and Measurement	● **clock face** Lesson 21.2 ● **Number Lines (by ones)** Lesson 21.2

Teacher Notes

Notes & Reflections

Unit 1 Performance Assessment

An Amusement Park

Task Summary The Unit 1 Performance Assessment will have students:

- Recognize a digit in one place is ten times what it is in the place to its right.
- Compare multi-digit whole numbers.
- Write multi-digit whole numbers using base-ten numerals, number names, and expanded form.
- Fluently add and subtract multi-digit whole numbers.

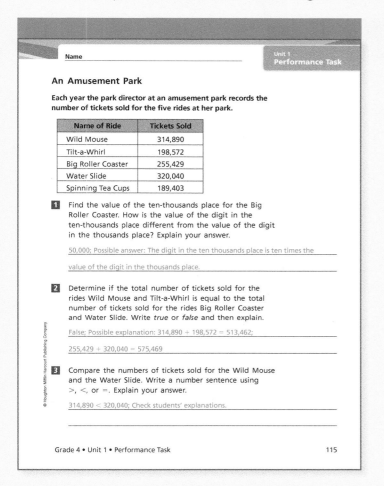

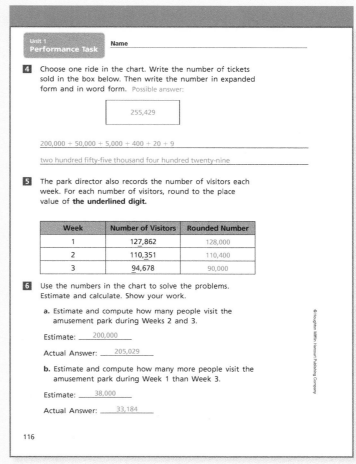

If students encounter difficulties in completing any of the tasks, use the information below to aid in interpreting student performance and to identify suggestions for follow-up and intervention.

Item	Content Focus	DOK	Intervene with
1	Recognize a digit in one place is ten times what it is in the place to its right.	1	Reteach 1.1
2	Fluently add multi-digit whole numbers.	2	Reteach 2.3
3	Compare multi-digit whole numbers.	2	Reteach 1.4
4	Write multi-digit whole numbers.	2	Reteach 1.2
5	Use place value understanding to round multi-digit whole numbers.	1	Reteach 1.5
6a	Use place value understanding to round multi-digit whole numbers. Fluently add and subtract multi-digit whole numbers.	2	Reteach 1.5 Reteach 2.1
6b	Use place value understanding to round multi-digit whole numbers. Fluently add and subtract multi-digit whole numbers.		Reteach 2.2

Additional teacher support and a scoring rubric can be found in your Assessment Guide.

Unit 2 Performance Assessment

Cars, Trains, Buses, and Planes

Task Summary The Unit 2 Performance Assessment will have students:

- Represent verbal statements of multiplicative comparison as multiplication equations.
- Assess the reasonableness of answers using estimation strategies including rounding.
- Multiply up to 4-digit numbers by 1-digit numbers.
- Find quotients and remainders with up to 4-digit dividends and 1-digit divisors.

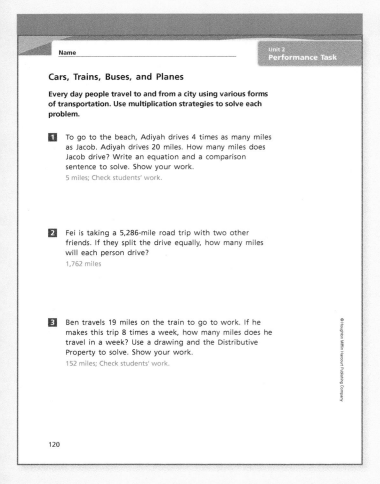

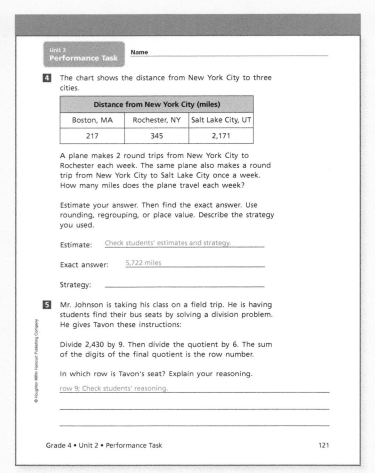

If students encounter difficulties in completing any of the tasks, use the information below to aid in interpreting student performance and to identify suggestions for follow-up and intervention.

Item	Content Focus	DOK	Intervene with
1	Represent verbal statements of multiplicative comparison as multiplication equations. Multiply or divide to solve problems involving multiplicative comparison.	1	Reteach 3.1 Reteach 3.3
2	Find quotients with up to 4-digit dividends and 1-digit divisors.	2	Reteach 7.3
3	Multiply up to 4-digit numbers by 1-digit numbers.	2	Reteach 5.2
4	Multiply up to 4-digit numbers by 1-digit numbers. Solve multistep problems using the four operations.	3	Reteach 5.6 Reteach 5.7
5	Find quotients with up to 4-digit dividends and 1-digit divisors. Solve multistep problems using the four operations.	2	Reteach 7.3 Reteach 7.4

Additional teacher support and a scoring rubric can be found in your Assessment Guide.

Unit 3 Performance Assessment

Visiting New York City

Task Summary The Unit 3 Performance Assessment will have students:

- Multiply two 2-digit numbers.
- Solve multistep word problems using the four operations.
- Estimate and assess reasonableness of answers.
- Apply the area formula for rectangles in problems.

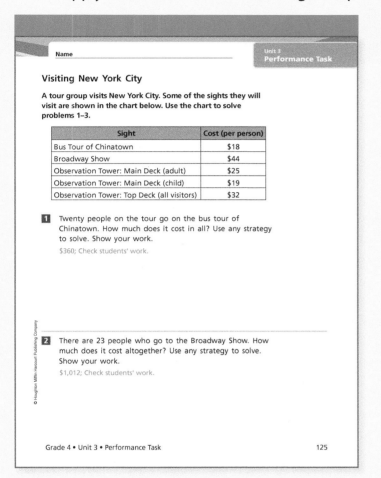

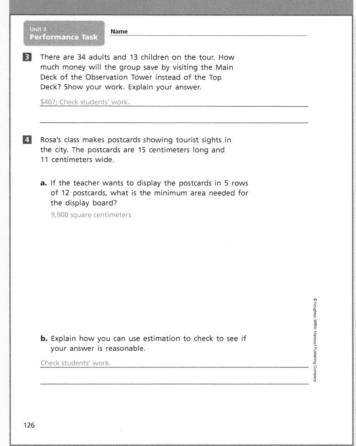

If students encounter difficulties in completing any of the tasks, use the information below to aid in interpreting student performance and to identify suggestions for follow-up and intervention.

Item	Content Focus	DOK	Intervene with
1	Multiply two 2-digit numbers.	2	Reteach 8.1 Reteach 8.6
2	Multiply two 2-digit numbers.	2	Reteach 8.4 Reteach 8.5 Reteach 8.6
3	Multiply two 2-digit numbers. Solve multistep word problems using the four operations.	3	Reteach 8.6 Reteach 8.7
4a 4b	Apply the area formula for rectangles in problems. Estimate and assess reasonableness multiplying two 2-digit numbers.	3	Reteach 8.7 Reteach 9.1 Reteach 9.4

Additional teacher support and a scoring rubric can be found in your Assessment Guide.

Unit 4 Performance Assessment

Have a Seat!

Task Summary The Unit 4 Performance Assessment will have students:

- Compare two fractions with different numerators and different denominators.
- Recognize and generate equivalent fractions.
- Use decimal notation for fractions with denominators 10 or 100.
- Compare two decimals to hundredths.
- Use the four operations to solve word problems involving money.

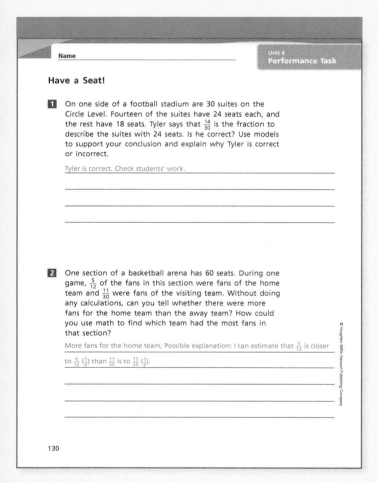

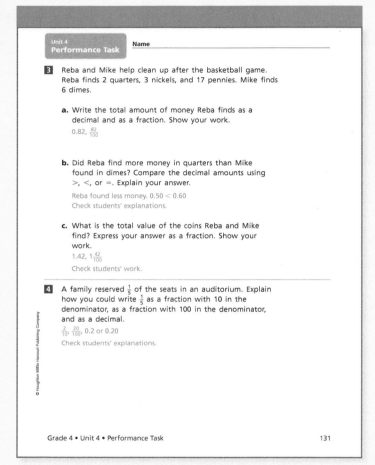

If students encounter difficulties in completing any of the tasks, use the information below to aid in interpreting student performance and to identify suggestions for follow-up and intervention.

Item	Content Focus	DOK	Intervene with
1	Recognize and generate equivalent fractions.	3	Reteach 11.1
2	Compare two fractions with different numerators and different denominators. Compare and order fractions.	2	Reteach 11.2 Reteach 11.6
3a 3b 3c	Use the four operations to solve word problems involving money. Compare two decimals to hundredths. Use the four operations to solve word problems involving money.	2	Reteach 12.4 Reteach 12.5 Reteach 12.6
4	Recognize and generate equivalent fractions. Use decimal notation for fractions with denominators 10 or 100.	2	Reteach 11.5 Reteach 12.1 Reteach 12.2

Additional teacher support and a scoring rubric can be found in your Assessment Guide.

Unit 5 Performance Assessment

Lending a Hand

Task Summary The Unit 5 Performance Assessment will have students:

- Solve word problems involving addition and subtraction of fractions.
- Add and subtract mixed numbers with like denominators.
- Decompose a fraction into a sum of fractions with the same denominator.
- Multiply a fraction by a whole number.
- Add two fractions with respective denominators 10 and 100.

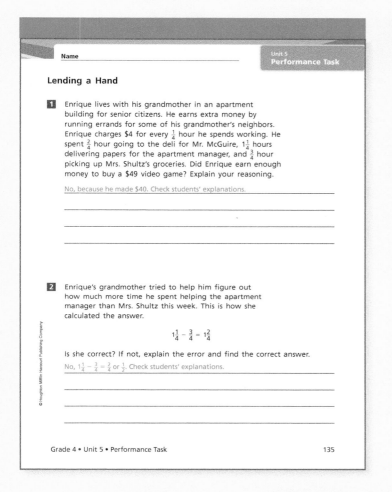

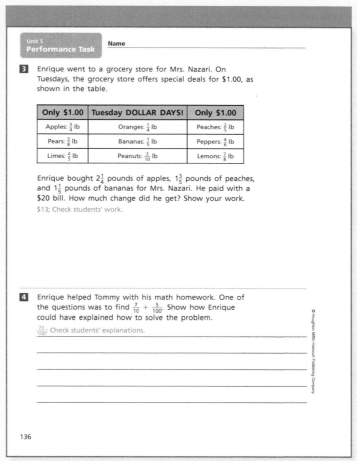

If students encounter difficulties in completing any of the tasks, use the information below to aid in interpreting student performance and to identify suggestions for follow-up and intervention.

Item	Content Focus	DOK	Intervene with
1	Rename a mixed number as a fraction greater than 1. Add mixed numbers with like denominators. Understand a fraction $\frac{a}{b}$ as a multiple of $\frac{1}{b}$.	3	Reteach 15.2 Reteach 15.3 Reteach 16.1
2	Subtract mixed numbers with like denominators.	3	Reteach 15.3 Reteach 15.4
3	Rename a mixed number as a fraction greater than 1. Decompose a fraction into a sum of fractions with the same denominator.	2	Reteach 15.2
4	Add two fractions with respective denominators 10 and 100.	2	Reteach 14.6

Additional teacher support and a scoring rubric can be found in your Assessment Guide.

Unit 6 Performance Assessment

Quilting Bee

Task Summary The Unit 6 Performance Assessment will have students:

- Draw and identify points, lines, line segments, rays, angles (right, acute, obtuse), and perpendicular and parallel lines.
- Identify line-symmetric figures and draw lines of symmetry.
- Generate a shape pattern that follows a given rule.

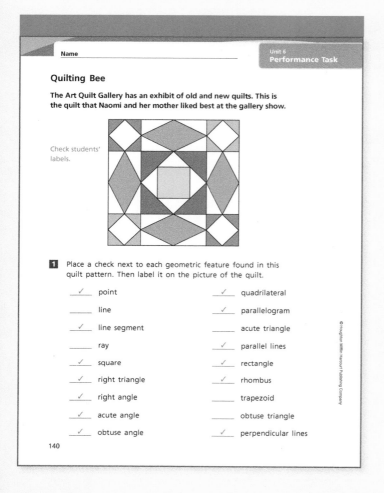

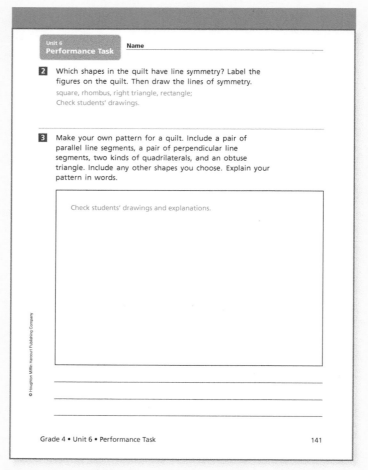

If students encounter difficulties in completing any of the tasks, use the information below to aid in interpreting student performance and to identify suggestions for follow-up and intervention.

Item	Content Focus	DOK	Intervene with
1	Identify points, lines, line segments, rays, angles (right, acute, obtuse), and perpendicular and parallel lines.	2	Reteach 17.1 Reteach 17.2 Reteach 17.4
2	Identify line-symmetric figures and draw lines of symmetry.	2	Reteach 18.1 Reteach 18.2
3	Generate a shape pattern that follows a given rule.	2	Reteach 18.3

Additional teacher support and a scoring rubric can be found in your Assessment Guide.

Unit 7 Performance Assessment

Store Storage

Task Summary The Unit 7 Performance Assessment will have students:

- Express measurements in a larger unit in terms of a smaller unit.
- Make a line plot to display a data set of measurements in fractions of a unit.
- Add and subtract fractions by using information presented in line plots.
- Solve word problems involving distances, intervals of time, and money.

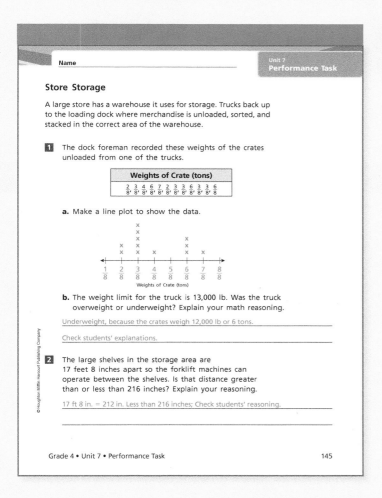

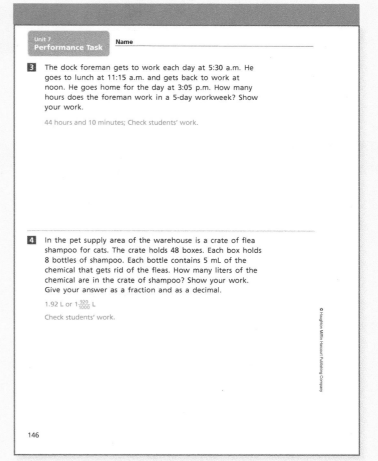

If students encounter difficulties in completing any of the tasks, use the information below to aid in interpreting student performance and to identify suggestions for follow-up and intervention.

Item	Content Focus	DOK	Intervene with
1a 1b	Make a line plot to display a data set of measurements in fractions of a unit. Add fractions by using information presented in line plots. Express measurements in a larger unit in terms of a smaller unit.	3	Reteach 19.3 Reteach 19.5
2	Express measurements in a larger unit in terms of a smaller unit.	2	Reteach 19.2
3	Solve word problems involving intervals of time.	2	Reteach 21.2
4	Solve word problems involving measurements.	2	Reteach 20.3 Reteach 20.4

Additional teacher support and a scoring rubric can be found in your Assessment Guide.

Into Math Solutions and Components

Core Materials

Student Materials

ONLINE
- Access all program materials
- Complete and submit assignments and assessments
- Assign Interactive Practice with Hints, Corrective Feedback, and Try Again support
- Track progress

Student Edition*
Multi-volume: write-in, consumable

Practice and Homework Journal*
One volume: write-in, consumable

Teacher Materials

ONLINE
- Access all program materials
- Plan lessons
- Assign materials
- View reports
- Group students and get recommendations
- Access immediate scores / item analysis
- Access reports on standards and skills

Teacher Edition
Conveniently sized for at-home planning

Planning and Pacing Guide
Correlations, resources, and pacing

Module Support Videos
Classroom videos featuring learning tasks, Language Routines, Talk Moves, and differentiation

Assessments

ONLINE
- Access and assign Math Growth Measure interim assessment
- Access and assign digital assessments and reports

Assessment Guide*
Secure assessment masters for teachers, including Form A and Form B for every module

Getting Ready for High Stakes Assessment*
High Stakes Assessment readiness practice for every Math Standard, with three half-length Practice Tests

*All print and digital student-facing materials are available in Spanish.

Differentiation and Support Materials

ONLINE

 Digital and interactive versions of resources are available on Ed: Your Friend in Learning.

ONLINE

- Math Center Activities
- Fluency Checks
- Digital Readers
- Poggles Digital Game
- Multilingual Glossary
- Digital Toolbox
- Math on the Spot tutorial videos
- School Home Letters

MathBoard

Write-on / wipe-off

Readers

With Lexile® scores

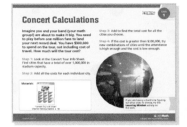

Unit Project Cards

Featuring STEM and careers

ONLINE

- Math Center Activities
- Interactive Reteach, Challenge, Additional Practice, and RtI
- Interactive Fluency Checks
- Digital Readers
- Poggles Digital Game
- Getting Ready for High Stakes Assessment Checks
- MTSS/RtI Tier 2 and Tier 3 Materials

Differentiated Instruction*

Reteach, Challenge, Additional Practice, Fluency

Tabletop Flipchart

Mini-lessons for reteaching to targeted small groups

Vocabulary Cards and Games*

Meaningful and fun activities

Classroom Manipulatives Kit

Hands-on materials

Differentiated Centers

Math Center organizers

Professional Learning and Implementation Support

ONLINE

- Getting Started Module
- Professional Learning Guide provided during implementation training

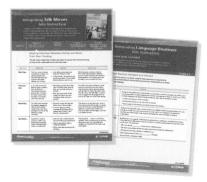

Professional Learning Cards

Feature Talk Moves and Language Routines

Getting Started Module and Professional Learning Guide

Implementation support

Academic Notebooks and Math Journals

Into Math has a variety of options to help students summarize learning. The Practice and Homework Journal includes several page types that students can add to Academic Notebooks or Math Journals.

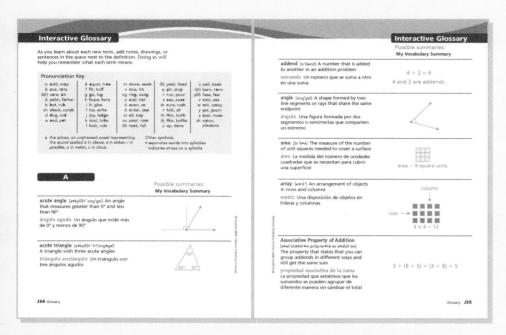

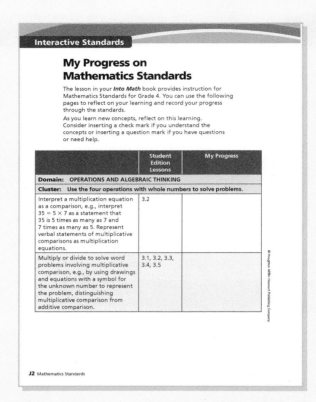

Students should add to their Interactive Glossary throughout the year as they develop understanding for each term. See the complete Interactive Glossary on pp. PG116–PG128.

Use the Interactive Standards Chart to record mastery of each standard.

Students can use the My Learning Summary pages to create their own Anchor Charts.

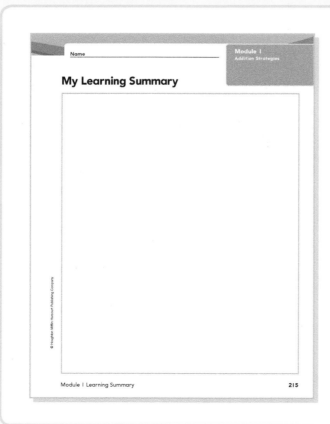

Anchor Charts can be developed throughout a module and placed on the classroom wall.

Place Value

THOUSANDS			ONES		
Hundreds	Tens	ones	Hundreds	Tens	ones
	1	1,	7	2	9

11,729
The value of the digit 7 is 7 hundreds.

Compare Numbers

THOUSANDS			ONES		
Hundreds	Tens	ones	Hundreds	Tens	ones
4	2	6,	5	7	9
4	3	6,	7	9	8

2 ten thousands is less than 3 ten thousands, so 426,579 < 436,798.

Place Value and Rounding

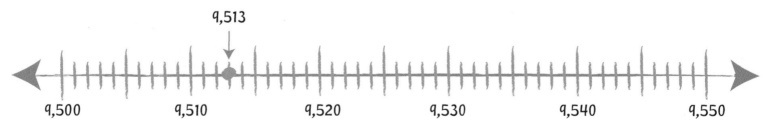

9,513 is closer to 9,510 than 9,520,
so 9,513 rounded to the nearest ten is 9,510.

Adding Whole Numbers

$$\begin{array}{r} \overset{1\ \ 11}{460{,}112} \\ +\ 201{,}998 \\ \hline 662{,}110 \end{array}$$

Subtracting Whole Numbers

$$\begin{array}{r} 793{,}445 \\ -\ 532{,}235 \\ \hline 261{,}210 \end{array}$$

Bar Model

Beth ate 8 grapes. She ate 5 grapes, then ate some more.

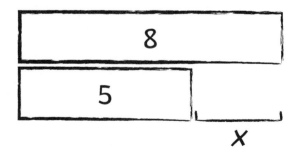

Perimeter of a Rectangle

$$P = l + w + l + w$$

5 inches

3 inches

$$P = 5 + 3 + 5 + 3$$
$$P = 16$$

The perimeter of the rectangle is 16 inches.

Multiplicative Comparison Problems

Marco takes 3 photos. Haley takes 3 times as many photos as Marco. How many photos does Haley take?

Drawing

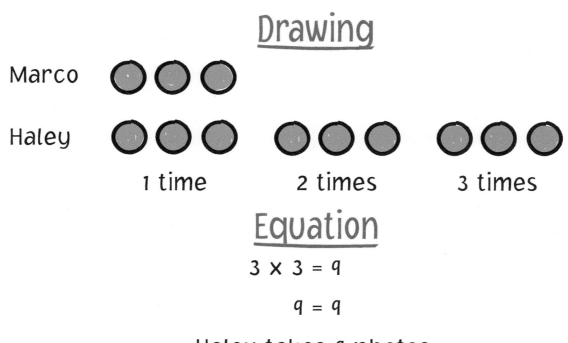

Equation

$$3 \times 3 = 9$$

$$9 = 9$$

Haley takes 9 photos.

- -

Sam takes 8 photos. Mina takes 2 photos. How many times as many photos does Sam take as Mina?

Bar Model

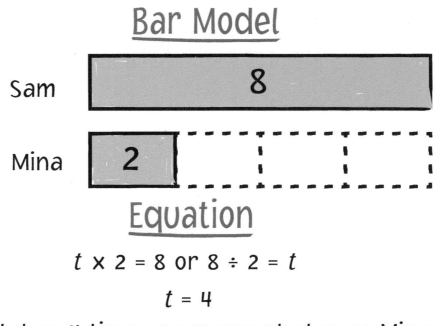

Equation

$$t \times 2 = 8 \text{ or } 8 \div 2 = t$$

$$t = 4$$

Sam takes 4 times as many photos as Mina.

Patterns • Mental Math • Estimation

Multiplication with Multiples of 10

5 × 7 = 35	Basic Fact
5 × 70 = 350	Multiple of 10
5 × 700 = 3,500	Multiple of 100
5 × 7,000 = 35,000	Multiple of 1,000

Estimating Products

Round to estimate

5 × 475 round 5 × 500

5 × 500 = 2,500

The answer is about 2,500.

8 × 345 = 2,760

Find two estimates that the exact product is between.

8 × 300 = 2,400   10 × 345 = 3,450

2,760 is between 2,400 and 3,450.

The answer is reasonable.

Division with Multiples of 10

24 ÷ 3 = 8	Basic Fact
240 ÷ 3 = 80	Multiple of 10
2,400 ÷ 3 = 800	Multiple of 100
24,000 ÷ 3 = 8,000	Multiple of 1,000

Estimating Quotients

Use compatible numbers to estimate

310 ÷ 5 ⟶ 300 ÷ 5

300 ÷ 5 = 60

The answer is about 60.

432 ÷ 6 = 72

Find two estimates that the exact quotient is between.

420 ÷ 6 = 70   480 ÷ 6 = 80

72 is between 70 and 80.

The answer is reasonable.

Mental Math Strategies

Use the Commutative Property

5 × 7 × 200 = 7 × 5 × 200

= 7 × 1,000

= 7,000

Use the Distributive Property

4 × 53 = (4 × 50) + (4 × 3)

= 200 + 12

= 212

Use Multiplication

720 ÷ 9 = ▢

Think: What times 9 equals 720?

9 × 8 = 72, so 9 × 80 = 720.

720 ÷ 9 = 80

Use Addition

327 ÷ 3 = ▢

Think: 327 = 300 + 27

327 ÷ 3 = (300 ÷ 3) + (27 ÷ 3)

= 100 + 9

= 109

Base-Ten Blocks

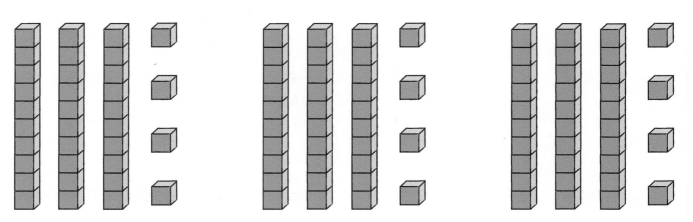

3 tens + 3 tens + 3 tens = 9 tens

4 ones + 4 ones + 4 ones = 12 ones = 1 ten + 2 ones

9 tens + 1 ten + 2 ones = 10 tens + 2 ones = 102

Area Model

	30	4
3		

$3 \times 30 = 90$

$3 \times 4 = 12$

$90 + 12 = 102$

Expanded Form

$3 \times 34 = 3 \times (30 + 4) = 3 \times 30 + 3 \times 4 = 90 + 12 = 102$

Partial Products

	20	3
6	120	18

$$\begin{array}{r} 23 \\ \times\ \ 6 \\ \hline 120 \\ 18 \\ \hline 138 \end{array}$$

120 ← 6 × 20

18 ← 6 × 3

Divide with 1-Digit Divisors

remainder – the amount left over after making equal groups
partial quotients – a method of dividing where multiples of the divisor are
subtracted from the dividend

Area Model

$72 \div 3 = 24$

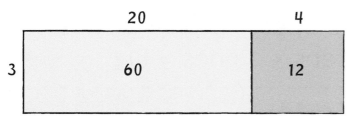

$60 \div 3 = 20$ $12 \div 3 = 4$

$20 + 4 = 24$

Distributive Property

$138 \div 6 = 23$

$138 = 120 + 18$

$138 \div 6 = (120 + 18) \div 6$

$\qquad = (120 \div 6) + (18 \div 6)$

$\qquad = 20 + 3$

$\qquad = 23$

Equal Groups

$81 \div 7$ is 11 r4.

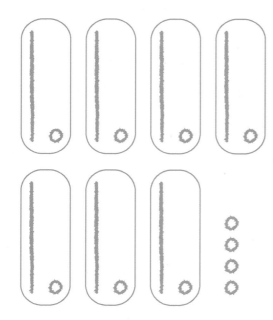

Partial Quotients

$925 \div 4$ is 231 r1.

$$4\overline{)925}$$

$- \ 800 \qquad 4 \times 200$

$\overline{\ 125}$

$- \ 120 \qquad 4 \times 30 \qquad\qquad 200$

$\overline{\ \ \ 5} \qquad\qquad\qquad\qquad\quad 30$

$\qquad\qquad\qquad\qquad\qquad\qquad +\ \ \ 1$

$- \ \ \ 4 \qquad 4 \times 1 \qquad\qquad \overline{\ 231}$

$\overline{\ \ \ 1}$

Dividing By 1-Digit Divisors

Place-Value Models

Divide 56 ÷ 4:

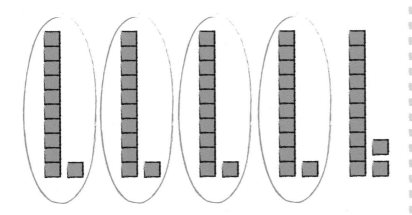

Regroup 1 ten as 10 ones.
Divide the ones.

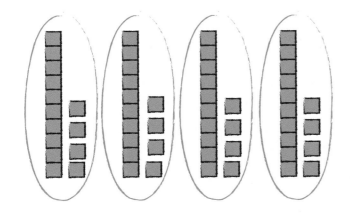

$56 \div 4 = 14$

Long Division

```
        1, 0   3   8  r3
   4 ) 4, 1   5   5
   −   4
       0   1
     −     0
           1   5
     −     1   2
               3   5
             −     3   2
                       3
```

Check:

$$\begin{array}{r} 1,038 \\ \times \quad 4 \\ \hline 4,152 \end{array} \qquad \begin{array}{r} 4,152 \\ + \quad 3 \\ \hline 4,155 \end{array}$$

Multiply by 2-Digit Numbers

Distributive Property

$30 \times 57 = 30 \times (50 + 7)$
$= (30 \times 50) + (30 \times 7)$
$= 1{,}500 + 210$
$= 1{,}710$

- -

Area Model

16 × 28

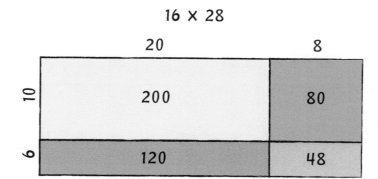

200 + 80 + 120 + 48 = 448

- -

Partial Products

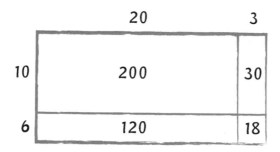

```
   23
 × 16
  200  ←——— 10 × 2 tens = 20 tens
   30  ←——— 10 × 3 ones = 30 ones
  120  ←——— 6 × 2 tens = 12 tens
 + 18  ←——— 6 × 3 ones = 18 ones
  368
```

© Houghton Mifflin Harcourt Publishing Company

Area Formula

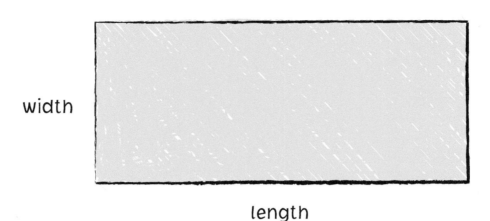

width

length

$$\text{area} = \text{length} \times \text{width}$$
$$A = l \times w$$

Solve Problems Using the Area Formula

- Find the area of a retangle.
- Find an unknown dimension.
- Find the area of figures that can be separated into rectangles.

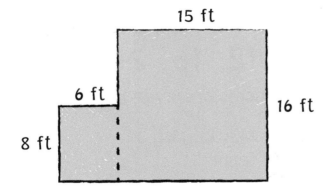

15 ft

6 ft

16 ft

8 ft

$A = 8 \times 6 + 16 \times 15$
$A = 48 + 240$
$A = 288$ square feet

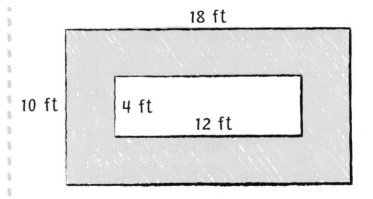

18 ft

10 ft

4 ft

12 ft

Outside rectangle: $A = 18 \times 10$
$A = 180$ square feet
Inside rectangle: $A = 12 \times 4$
$A = 48$ square feet
Shaded region: $A = 180 - 48$
$A = 132$ square feet

Number Theory

Factors and Multiples

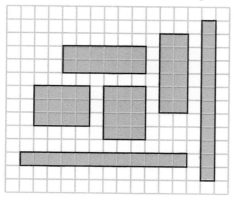

Factors of 12 are 1, 2, 3, 4, 6 and 12.

Factor pairs: 1 and 12, 2 and 6, 3 and 4
12 is a multiple of 1, 2, 3, 4, 6, and 12.

If 4 is a factor of 12, then 12 is a multiple of 4.

Prime and Composite

A prime number has only 1 and itself as factors. A composite number has more than two factors.

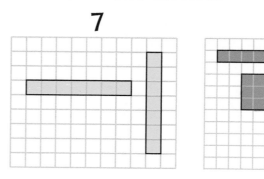

7 is a prime number because it has only 1 and itself as factors.

9 is a composite number because it has more than two factors.

Divisibility

Divisibility Rules	
A number is divisible by...	If...
2	the number is even.
3	the sum of the digits is divisible by 3.
4	the last two digits are divisible by 4.
5	the last digit is 0 or 5.
6	the number is divisible by 2 and 3.
9	the sum of the digits is divisible by 9.

If 4 is divisible by 20, then 4 is a factor of 20 and 20 is a multiple of 4.

Number Patterns

Rule: Add 4.
First term: 8

$$\overset{+4}{\longrightarrow}\ \overset{+4}{\longrightarrow}\ \overset{+4}{\longrightarrow}\ \overset{+4}{\longrightarrow}$$

8, 12, 16, 20, 24

All terms are even numbers.

Rule: Multiply by 3.
First term: 5

$$\overset{\times 3}{\longrightarrow}\ \overset{\times 3}{\longrightarrow}\ \overset{\times 3}{\longrightarrow}\ \overset{\times 3}{\longrightarrow}$$

5, 15, 45, 135, 405

All terms are odd numbers and have the digit 5 in the ones place.

Compare Fractions

Using Visual Models

$\frac{1}{3}$	$\frac{1}{3}$	$\frac{1}{3}$

$\frac{1}{3}$

$\frac{1}{5}$	$\frac{1}{5}$	$\frac{1}{5}$	$\frac{1}{5}$	$\frac{1}{5}$

$\frac{3}{5}$

$$\frac{1}{3} < \frac{3}{5}$$

Using Benchmarks

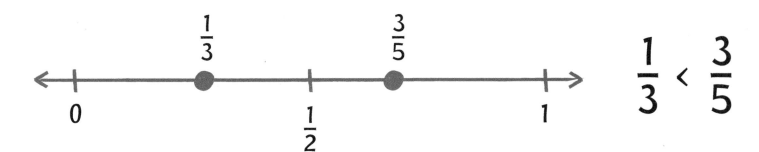

$$\frac{1}{3} < \frac{3}{5}$$

Using Equivalent Fractions

$$\frac{1}{3} = \frac{5}{15}$$

$$\frac{3}{5} = \frac{9}{15}$$

$$\frac{5}{15} < \frac{9}{15}, \text{ so } \frac{1}{3} < \frac{3}{5}.$$

Relate Fractions and Decimals

Tenths

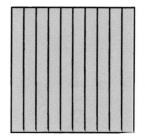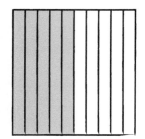

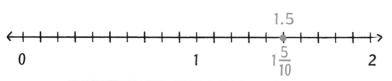

1.5

Ones	.	Tenths	Hundredths
1	.	5	

$1\frac{5}{10} = 1.5$

Compare Decimals

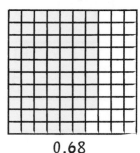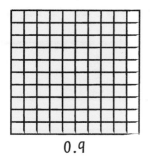

0.68   0.9

0.68   0.9

Ones	.	Tenths	Hundredths
0	.	6	8
0	.	9	

0.68 < 0.9

Hundredths

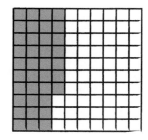

0.37

$\frac{37}{100}$

Ones	.	Tenths	Hundredths
0	.	3	7

$\frac{37}{100} = 0.37$

Fractions, Decimals, and Money

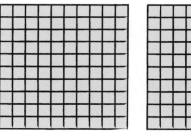

Ones	.	Tenths	Hundredths
1	.	7	5

cents: 175¢   mixed number: 1.75
decimal: 1.75   decimal dollar
                       amount: $1.75

Use Fractions to Understand Angles

Points, Lines, Line Segments, and Angles

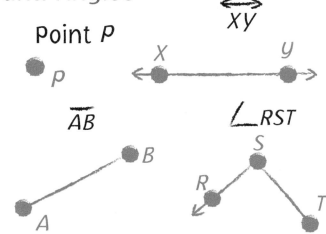

Point P

$\overleftrightarrow{XY}$

$\overline{AB}$

$\angle RST$

Angle Degrees and Fractional Parts of a Circle

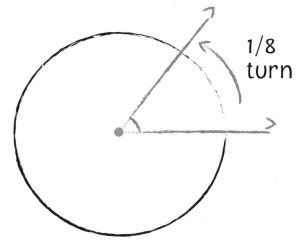

1/8 turn

Measure and Draw Angles

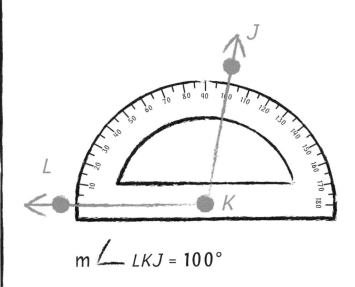

$m\angle LKJ = 100°$

Join and Separate Angles

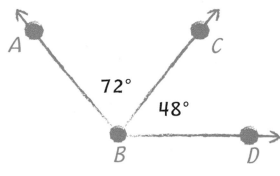

72°

48°

$m\angle ABC + m\angle CBD = m\angle ABD$

72°   +   48°   =   120°

Represent and Model Addition of Fractions

- Break apart fractions into two fractions with like denominators.

- Join two fractions that have the same whole.

1

$\frac{1}{8}$	$\frac{1}{8}$	$\frac{1}{8}$	$\frac{1}{8}$	$\frac{1}{8}$	$\frac{1}{8}$	$\frac{1}{8}$	$\frac{1}{8}$

$$\frac{3}{8} + \frac{1}{8} = \frac{4}{8}$$

- -

Represent and Model Subtraction of Fractions

- Compare fractions to determine how much more.

- Take away a fraction of a whole from a greater fraction of the same whole.

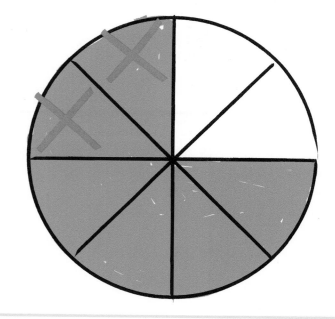

$$\frac{6}{8} - \frac{2}{8} = \frac{4}{8}$$

© Houghton Mifflin Harcourt Publishing Company

Fractions Greater Than 1

Rename Fractions as Mixed Numbers

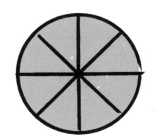 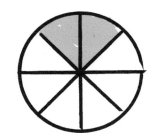 $= \dfrac{10}{8} = 1\dfrac{2}{8}$

1	1
$\frac{1}{4}$ $\frac{1}{4}$ $\frac{1}{4}$ $\frac{1}{4}$	$\frac{1}{4}$ $\frac{1}{4}$ $\frac{1}{4}$ $\frac{1}{4}$

$= \dfrac{6}{4} = 1\dfrac{2}{4}$

$$\dfrac{19}{5} = \dfrac{5}{5} + \dfrac{5}{5} + \dfrac{5}{5} + \dfrac{4}{5} = 3\dfrac{4}{5}$$

Rename to Add and Subtract Mixed Numbers

$$1\dfrac{5}{8} + 2\dfrac{2}{8} = \dfrac{13}{8} + \dfrac{18}{8} = \dfrac{31}{8} = 3\dfrac{7}{8}$$

$$6\dfrac{3}{4} - 4\dfrac{1}{4} = \dfrac{27}{4} - \dfrac{17}{4} = \dfrac{10}{4} = 2\dfrac{2}{4}$$

Multiply Fractions by Whole Numbers

Represent Multiples of Unit Fractions

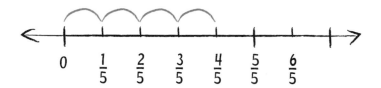

$$\frac{1}{5} + \frac{1}{5} + \frac{1}{5} + \frac{1}{5} = \frac{4}{5}$$

$$4 \times \frac{1}{5} = \frac{4}{5}$$

Represent Multiples of Fractions

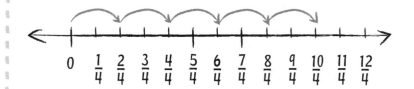

$$5 \times \frac{2}{4} = \frac{10}{4}$$

Represent Multiplication of Fractions by Whole Numbers

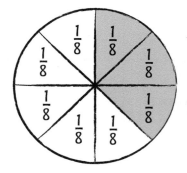 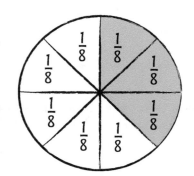

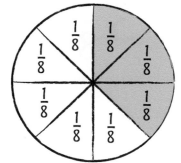

3 groups of $\frac{3}{8}$

$$3 \times \frac{3}{8} = 3 \times 3 \times \frac{1}{8} = \frac{9}{8} = 1\frac{1}{8}$$

Solve Multiplication Problems with Mixed Numbers

$$3 \times 2\frac{3}{4} = \boxed{}$$

Write the mixed number as a fraction greater than 1:

$$2\frac{3}{4} = \frac{11}{4}$$

Find the product:

$$3 \times \frac{11}{4} = \frac{33}{4}$$

Write the product as a mixed number:

$$\frac{33}{4} = 8\frac{1}{4}$$

Two-Dimensional Figures

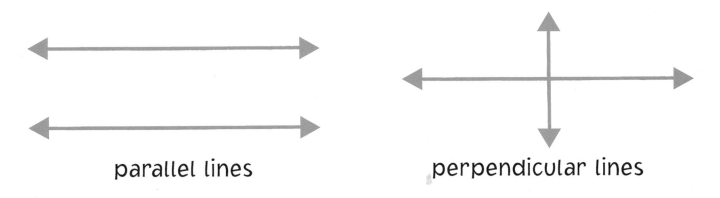

parallel lines

perpendicular lines

Types of Triangles

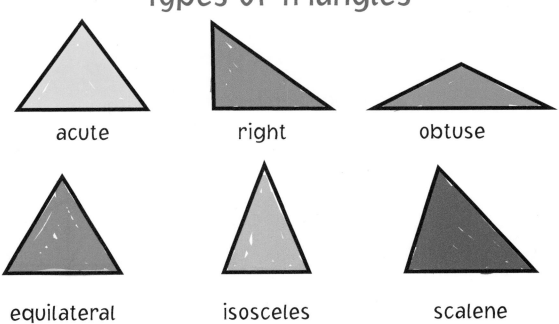

acute

right

obtuse

equilateral

isosceles

scalene

Types of Quadrilaterals

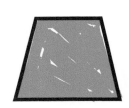

trapezoid

parallelogram

rhombus

rectangle

square

Line Symmetry

A line of symmetry is an imaginary line that can divide a figure into two parts that match exactly.

If a figure has a line of symmetry, it is said to have line symmetry.

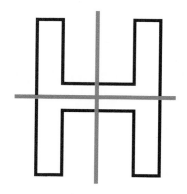 

Line Symmetry for Regular Polygons

A regular polygon has all sides equal in length and all angles equal in measure.

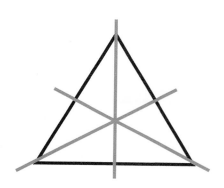 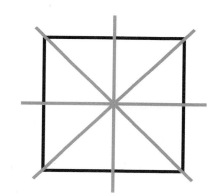 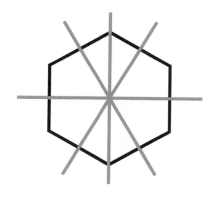

Shape Patterns

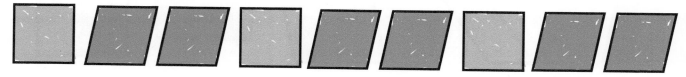

Rule: *1 orange square, 2 blue rhombuses*
Next three figures: orange square, blue rhombus, blue rhombus

Benchmarks

1 inch is about the length of 1 thumb print
1 foot is about the distance from wrist to elbow
1 yard is about the distance from fingertip to fingertip with arms stretched out
1 cup holds about the same as a small mug
1 pint holds about the same as a large glass

Vocabulary

inch (in.)   pound (lb)
foot (ft)   ton (T)
yard (yd)   ounce (oz)
mile (mi)   liquid
cup (c)   volume
pint (pt)   line plot
fluid ounce (fl oz)
quart (qt)
gallon (gal)

Line Plot

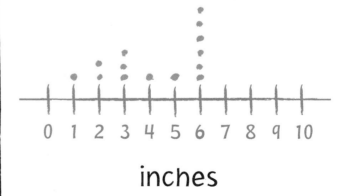

Height of Plant

0 1 2 3 4 5 6 7 8 9 10

inches

Metric Units

Length

millimeter: Tiny! about the thickness of a credit card

centimeter: about the width of a finger

decimeter: about the length of a new crayon

meter: about the width of a door frame

kilometer: distance you can walk in about 10 minutes

Liquid Volume

milliliter: Tiny! about the amount of liquid in an eyedropper

liter: about the amount of liquid in a large water bottle

Mass

milligram: Tiny! about the mass of 3 grains of salt

gram: about the mass of a paper clip

kilogram: about the mass of a baseball bat

Time and Measurement

Compare Hours, Minutes, and Seconds

- 1 hour = 60 minutes
- 1 minute = 60 seconds

hours	minutes
1	60
2	120
3	180
4	240
5	300

minutes	seconds
1	60
2	120
3	180
4	240
5	300

3:40:23

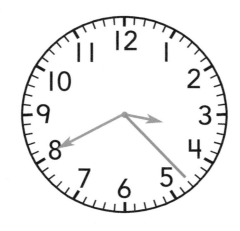

Think: Regroup minutes and seconds into groups of 60.

Find Elapsed Time

Start Time
+ Elapsed Time
_____
End Time

End Time
− Start Time
_____
Elapsed Time

End Time
− Elapsed Time
_____
Start Time

- What information do you know?
- What information do you need to know?

Practice with Mixed Measures

- Change yards to feet: 4 yards x 3 = 12 feet
- Change feet to inches: 12 feet x 12 = 144 inches
- Change kilometers to meters: 10 km x 1,000 = 10,000 m
- Change meters to centimeters: 10 m x 100 = 1,000 cm

Interactive Glossary

As you learn about each new term, add notes, drawings, or sentences in the space next to the definition. Doing so will help you remember what each term means.

Pronunciation Key

a add, map	ē equal, tree	m move, seem	ōō pool, food	ù pull, book
ā ace, rate	f fit, half	n nice, tin	p pit, stop	û(r) burn, term
â(r) care, air	g go, log	ng ring, song	r run, poor	yōō fuse, few
ä palm, father	h hope, hate	o odd, hot	s see, pass	v vain, eve
b bat, rub	i it, give	ō open, so	sh sure, rush	w win, away
ch check, catch	ī ice, write	ô order, jaw	t talk, sit	y yet, yearn
d dog, rod	j joy, ledge	oi oil, boy	th thin, both	z zest, muse
e end, pet	k cool, take	ou pout, now	th this, bathe	zh vision,
	l look, rule	ōō took, full	u up, done	pleasure

ə the schwa, an unstressed vowel representing the sound spelled a in above, e in sicken, i in possible, o in melon, u in circus

Other symbols:
• separates words into syllables
′ indicates stress on a syllable

A

acute angle [ə•kyōōt′ ang′gəl] An angle that measures greater than 0° and less than 90°

ángulo agudo Un ángulo que mide más de 0° y menos de 90°

Possible summaries:
My Vocabulary Summary

acute triangle [ə•kyōōt′ trī′ang•gəl] A triangle with three acute angles

triángulo acutángulo Un triángulo con tres ángulos agudos

© Houghton Mifflin Harcourt Publishing Company

Interactive Glossary

addend [a′dend] A number that is added to another in an addition problem

sumando Un número que se suma a otro en una suma

Possible summaries:
My Vocabulary Summary

$4 + 2 = 6$

4 and 2 are addends.

angle [ang′gəl] A shape formed by two line segments or rays that share the same endpoint

ángulo Una figura formada por dos segmentos o semirrectas que comparten un extremo

area [âr′ē•ə] The measure of the number of unit squares needed to cover a surface

área La medida del número de unidades cuadradas que se necesitan para cubrir una superficie

area = 9 square units

array [ə•rā′] An arrangement of objects in rows and columns

matriz Una disposición de objetos en hileras y columnas

column

row

$3 \times 4 = 12$

Associative Property of Addition
[ə•sō′shē•āt•iv prŏp′ər•tē əv ə•dish′ən] The property that states that you can group addends in different ways and still get the same sum

propiedad asociativa de la suma La propiedad que establece que los sumandos se pueden agrupar de diferente manera sin cambiar el total

$3 + (8 + 5) = (3 + 8) + 5$

© Houghton Mifflin Harcourt Publishing Company

Interactive Glossary

Possible summaries:
My Vocabulary Summary

Associative Property of Multiplication
[ə•sō´shē•ə•tiv prŏp´ər•tē əv
mul•tə•pli•kā´shən] The property that states
that you can group factors in different
ways and still get the same product

propiedad asociativa de la
multiplicación La propiedad que
establece que los factores se pueden
agrupar de diferente manera sin cambiar
el producto

$3 \times (4 \times 2) = (3 \times 4) \times 2$

B

base [bās] A polygon's side

base Uno de los lados de un polígono

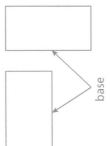

base

benchmark [bench´märk] A known size
or amount that helps you understand a
different size or amount

punto de referencia Un tamaño o una
cantidad que se conoce y que permite
comprender otro tamaño o cantidad

I can use the benchmark
fraction $\frac{1}{2}$ to compare fractions.

C

capacity [kə•pas´i•tē] The amount a
container can hold when filled

capacidad Cantidad que puede contener
un recipiente cuando se llena

My fish bowl has a capacity
of about 1 gallon.

Interactive Glossary

Possible summaries:
My Vocabulary Summary

common denominator [kŏm´ən
dē•nŏm´ə•nāt•ər] A common multiple of
two or more denominators

denominador común Múltiplo común de
dos o más denominadores

Some common denominators
for $\frac{1}{4}$ and $\frac{5}{6}$ are 12, 24, and 36.

common factor [kŏm´ən fak´tər] A number
that is a factor of two or more numbers

factor común Un número que es factor
de dos o más números

3 is a common factor of
6 and 9.

common multiple [kŏm´ən mul´tə•pəl]
A number that is a multiple of two or
more numbers

múltiplo común Un número que es un
múltiplo de dos o más números

15 is a common multiple
of 3 and 5.

Commutative Property of Addition
[kə•myōōt´ə•tiv prŏp´ər•tē əv ə•dish´ən] The
property that states that when the order
of two addends is changed, the sum is
the same

propiedad conmutativa de la suma
La propiedad que establece que, cuando
cambia el orden de dos sumandos, el
total es el mismo

$4 + 5 = 5 + 4$

Commutative Property of Multiplication
[kə•myōōt´ə•tiv prŏp´ər•tē əv mul•tə•pli•kā´shən]
The property that states that when the
order of two factors is changed, the
product is the same

propiedad conmutativa de la
multiplicación La propiedad que
establece que, cuando cambia el orden
de dos factores, el producto es el mismo

$4 \times 5 = 5 \times 4$

Interactive Glossary

Possible summaries:
My Vocabulary Summary

compatible numbers [kəm•pat′ə•bəl num′bərz] Numbers that are easy to compute mentally

números compatibles Números con los que es fácil hacer cálculos mentales

Estimate. 176 ÷ 8

160 divides easily by 8.
← compatible numbers

composite number [kəm•päz′it num′bər] A number having more than two factors

número compuesto Un número que tiene más de dos factores

6 is a composite number, since its factors are 1, 2, 3, and 6.

cup (c) [kup] A customary unit used to measure capacity and liquid volume;
1 cup = 8 fluid ounces

taza (tz) Una unidad del sistema usual con la que se mide la capacidad y el volumen de un líquido;
1 taza = 8 onzas fluidas

A mug of hot chocolate is about 1 cup.

D

decimal [des′ə•məl] A number with one or more digits to the right of the decimal point

decimal Número con uno o más dígitos a la derecha del punto decimal

4.5   0.9

decimal point [des′ə•məl point] A symbol used to separate dollars from cents in money amounts, and to separate the ones and the tenths places in a decimal

punto decimal Un símbolo que se usa para separar los dólares de los centavos en cantidades de dinero y el lugar de las unidades del lugar de los décimos en un número decimal

6.4
← decimal point

Interactive Glossary

Possible summaries:
My Vocabulary Summary

decimeter (dm) [des′i•mēt•ər] A metric unit for measuring length or distance;
1 meter = 10 decimeters

decímetro (dm) Una unidad del sistema métrico con la que se mide la longitud o la distancia;
1 metro = 10 decímetros

1 decimeter = 10 centimeters

A crayon is about 1 decimeter long.

degree (°) [di•grē′] The unit used for measuring angles and temperatures

grado (°) La unidad con la que se miden los ángulos y la temperatura

A right angle measures 90°.

denominator [dē•näm′ə•nāt•ər]
The number below the bar in a fraction that tells how many equal parts are in the whole or in the group

denominador El número que está debajo de la barra en una fracción y que indica cuántas partes iguales hay en el entero o en el grupo

$\frac{3}{4}$
← denominator

Distributive Property [di•strib′yōō•tiv prä′pər•tē] The property that states that multiplying a sum by a number is the same as multiplying each addend by the number and then adding the products

propiedad distributiva La propiedad que establece que multiplicar una suma por un número es igual que multiplicar cada sumando por ese número y luego sumar los productos

$5 \times (10 + 6) = (5 \times 10) + (5 \times 6)$
$(10 + 8) \div 2 = (10 \div 2) + (8 \div 2)$

divide [də•vīd′] To separate into equal groups; the opposite operation of multiplication

dividir Separar en grupos iguales; la operación opuesta a la multiplicación

12 ÷ 3 = 4

Interactive Glossary

Possible summaries:
My Vocabulary Summary

dividend [də•vi•dend] The number that is to be divided in a division problem

dividendo El número que se divide en una división

$$12 \div 3 = 4$$
$$3\overline{)12}\ \ 4$$
dividend   dividend

divisible [də•viz´ə•bəl] A number is divisible by another number if the whole-number quotient is a counting number and the remainder is zero.

divisible Un número es divisible entre otro número si el cociente de número entero es un número natural y el residuo es cero.

12 is divisible by 3 because $12 \div 3 = 4.$

divisor [də•vī´zer] The number that divides the dividend

divisor El número entre el que se divide el dividendo

$$12 \div 3 = 4$$
$$3\overline{)12}\ \ 4$$
divisor   divisor

E

elapsed time [ē•lapst´ tīm] The time that passes from the start of an activity to the end of that activity

tiempo transcurrido El tiempo que pasa desde el comienzo hasta el final de una actividad

+5 min +5 min +5 min +5 min +5 min
3:45 p.m. Start Time   3:50 p.m.   3:55 p.m.   4:00 p.m.   4:05 p.m. End Time

$$5 + 5 + 5 + 5 = 20$$
Elapsed time is 20 minutes.

endpoint [end´point] The point at either end of a line segment or the starting point of a ray

extremo El punto ubicado en cada punta de un segmento o el punto de inicio de una semirrecta

A   B   endpoint   K   L

Interactive Glossary

Possible summaries:
My Vocabulary Summary

equal parts [ē´kwəl pärts] Parts that are exactly the same size

partes iguales Partes que tienen exactamente el mismo tamaño

4 equal parts   4 equal parts

equilateral triangle [ē•kwi•lat´ər•əl trī´ang•gəl] A triangle with three sides of equal length

triángulo equilátero Triángulo con tres lados de la misma longitud

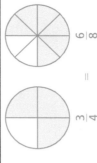

3 in.   3 in.   3 in.

equivalent decimals [ē•kwiv´ə•lənt des´ə•məlz] Two or more decimals that name the same amount

decimales equivalentes Dos o más decimales que representan la misma cantidad

0.8 and 0.80 are equivalent decimals.

equivalent fractions [ē•kwiv´ə•lənt frak´shənz] Two or more fractions that name the same amount

fracciones equivalentes Dos o más fracciones que indican la misma cantidad

$$\frac{3}{4} = \frac{6}{8}$$

estimate (noun) [es´tə•mit] A number that is close to the exact amount

estimación Un número cercano a la cantidad exacta

An estimate tells about how much or about how many.
My dog weighs about 25 pounds.

estimate (verb) [es´tə•māt] To find an answer that is close to the exact amount

estimar Hallar un resultado cercano a la cantidad exacta

To estimate is to name about how much or about how many.
I estimate the answer before dividing.

Possible summaries:
My Vocabulary Summary

expanded form [ek•span′did fôrm] A way to write numbers by showing the value of each digit

forma desarrollada Una manera de escribir los números mostrando el valor de cada dígito

$$3{,}212 = 3{,}000 + 200 + 10 + 2$$

F

factor [fak′tər] A number that is multiplied by another number to find a product

factor Un número que se multiplica por otro número para hallar un producto

$$7 \times 8 = 56$$
factors   product

factor pair [fak′tər pâr] Two factors that make a product

par de factores Dos factores que forman un producto

The factor pairs for 12 are:
1 and 12
2 and 6
3 and 4

fluid ounce (fl oz) [floo′id ouns]
A customary unit used to measure liquid capacity and liquid volume;
1 cup = 8 fluid ounces

onza fluida (oz fl) Una unidad del sistema usual con la que se mide la capacidad y el volumen líquido;
1 taza = 8 onzas fluidas

A glass of water is about 8 fluid ounces.

foot (ft) [foot] A customary unit used to measure length or distance;
1 foot = 12 inches

pie Unidad del sistema usual que se usa para medir la longitud o la distancia;
1 pie = 12 pulgadas

A sheet of paper is almost 1 foot long.

formula [fôr′myoo•lə] A set of symbols that expresses a mathematical rule

fórmula Un conjunto de símbolos que expresa una regla matemática

Area = length × width
or
$$A = l \times w$$

Possible summaries:
My Vocabulary Summary

G

gallon (gal) [gal′ən] A customary unit for measuring capacity and liquid volume;
1 gallon = 4 quarts

galón (gal) Una unidad del sistema usual con la que se mide la capacidad y el volumen líquido; 1 galón = 4 cuartos

A large jug of milk is about 1 gallon.

A fish tank holds about 10 gallons of water.

gram (g) [gram] A metric unit for measuring mass;
1 kilogram = 1,000 grams

gramo (g) Una unidad del sistema métrico con la que se mide la masa;
1 kilogramo = 1,000 gramos

A paper clip has a mass of about 1 gram.

A nickel has a mass of about 5 grams.

H

height [hīt] The measure of a perpendicular from the base to the top of a two-dimensional figure

altura La medida de una recta perpendicular desde la base hasta la parte superior de una figura bidimensional

height

base

hundredth [hun′drədth] One of one hundred equal parts

centésimo Una de cien partes iguales

hundredth

Written as a fraction:
$$\frac{1}{100}$$

Written as a decimal:
0.01

Possible summaries:
My Vocabulary Summary

I

inch (in.) [inch] A customary unit used to measure length or distance

pulgada (pulg) Unidad del sistema usual que se usa para medir la longitud o la distancia

1 inch

intersecting lines [in•tər•sekt′ing līnz] Lines that cross each other at exactly one point

líneas secantes Líneas que se cruzan entre sí en un único punto

inverse operations [in′vûrs ŏp•ər•ā′shənz] Operations that undo each other, such as addition and subtraction or multiplication and division

operaciones inversas Operaciones que se cancelan entre sí, como la suma y la resta o la multiplicación y la división

$6 \times 8 = 48$ and $48 \div 6 = 8$

isosceles triangle [ī•sŏs′ə•lēz trī′ang•gəl] A triangle with at least two sides of equal length

triángulo isósceles Triángulo con al menos dos lados de la misma longitud

10 in. 10 in. 7 in.

K

kilogram (kg) [kĭl′ō•gram] A metric unit for measuring mass; 1 kilogram = 1,000 grams

kilogramo (kg) Una unidad del sistema métrico con la que se mide la masa; 1 kilogramo = 1,000 gramos

A pineapple has a mass of about 1 kilogram.

A cat has a mass of about 5 kilograms.

Possible summaries:
My Vocabulary Summary

kilometer (km) [kə•lŏm′ət•ər] A metric unit for measuring length or distance; 1 kilometer = 1,000 meters

kilómetro (km) Una unidad del sistema métrico con la que se mide la longitud o la distancia; 1 kilómetro = 1,000 metros

I can walk 1 kilometer in about 10 minutes.

A 10-kilometer run is equal to 6.2 miles.

L

line [līn] A straight path of points in a plane that continues without end in both directions with no endpoints

línea Trayectoria recta que se extiende infinitamente en direcciones opuestas

S T

line of symmetry [līn əv sim′ə•trē] An imaginary line on a figure about which the figure can be folded so that its two parts match exactly

eje de simetría Una línea imaginaria a lo largo de la cual se puede plegar una figura de manera que sus dos partes coincidan totalmente

line of symmetry

line plot [līn plŏt] A graph that records each piece of data on a number line

diagrama de puntos Una gráfica en la que cada dato se registra sobre una recta numérica

Bean Seedlings

2 3 4 5 6 7 8 9 10
Height (in inches)

Interactive Glossary

line segment [lĭn sĕg'mənt] A part of a line that includes two points called endpoints and all the points between them

segmento Una parte de una recta que incluye dos puntos llamados extremos y todos los puntos que hay entre ellos

line symmetry [lĭn sĭm'ə•trē] What a figure has if it can be folded about a line so that its two parts match exactly

simetría axial Lo que tiene una figura si se puede plegar a lo largo de una línea de manera que sus dos partes coincidan totalmente

Possible summaries:
My Vocabulary Summary

A ———————• B

The arrow has line symmetry.

liquid volume [lĭk'wĭd väl'yōōm] The measure of the space a liquid occupies

volumen de un líquido La medida del espacio que ocupa un líquido

Liquid volume is how much liquid a container is holding.

liter (L) [lē'tər] A metric unit for measuring capacity and liquid volume; 1 liter = 1,000 milliliters

litro (l / L) Una unidad del sistema métrico con la que se mide la capacidad y el volumen líquido; 1 litro = 1,000 mililitros

A bottle of water is about 1 liter.

A bucket holds about 20 liters of water.

M

mass [măs] The amount of matter in an object

masa La cantidad de materia que hay en un objeto

A paper clip has a mass of about 1 gram.

J46 Glossary

© Houghton Mifflin Harcourt Publishing Company

Interactive Glossary

meter (m) [mēt'ər] A metric unit for measuring length or distance; 1 meter = 100 centimeters

metro (m) Una unidad del sistema métrico con la que se mide la longitud o la distancia; 1 metro = 100 centímetros

Possible summaries:
My Vocabulary Summary

A baseball bat is about 1 meter long.

mile (mi) [mīl] A customary unit for measuring length or distance; 1 mile = 5,280 feet

milla (mi) Una unidad del sistema usual con la que se mide la longitud o la distancia; 1 milla = 5,280 pies

I can run 1 mile in about 12 minutes.

Four laps around the track is about 1 mile.

milligram (mg) [mĭl'ĭ•grăm] A metric unit for measuring mass; 1,000 milligrams = 1 gram

miligramo Una unidad del sistema métrico con la que se mide la masa; 1,000 miligramo = 1 gramos

A grain of sand has a mass of about 1 milligram.

A paper clip has a mass of 1,000 milligrams.

milliliter (mL) [mĭl'ĭ•lēt•ər] A metric unit for measuring capacity and liquid volume; 1 liter = 1,000 milliliters

mililitro (mL) Una unidad del sistema métrico con la que se mide la capacidad y el volumen líquido; 1 litro = 1,000 mililitros

An eye dropper holds about 1 milliliter of liquid.

A bottle of water holds about 1,000 milliliters.

millimeter (mm) [mĭl'ĭ•mēt•ər] A metric unit for measuring length or distance; 1 centimeter = 10 millimeters

milímetro (mm) Una unidad del sistema métrico con la que se mide la longitud o la distancia; 1 centímetro = 10 milímetros

A pin is about 1 millimeter wide.

A finger is about 10 millimeters wide.

Glossary **J47**

© Houghton Mifflin Harcourt Publishing Company

Possible summaries:
My Vocabulary Summary

minute (min) [min′it] A unit used to measure short amounts of time;
1 minute = 60 seconds

There are 60 minutes in 1 hour.

minuto (min) Una unidad con la que se miden periodos breves de tiempo;
1 minuto = 60 segundos

I can do 50 jumping jacks in about 1 minute.

mixed number [mikst num′ber] An amount given as a whole number and a fraction

número mixto Una cantidad que se da como un número entero y una fracción

$1\frac{1}{4}$

multiple [mul′tə•pəl] A number that is the product of two counting numbers

múltiplo Número que es el producto de dos número naturales

$$\begin{array}{ccc} 3 & 3 & 3 \\ \times 1 & \times 2 & \times 3 \\ \hline 3 & 6 & 9 \end{array} \leftarrow \text{counting numbers} \\ \leftarrow \text{multiples of 3}$$

N

numerator [noo′mər•ā•ter] The number above the bar in a fraction that tells how many parts of the whole or group are being considered

numerador El número que está arriba de la barra en una fracción y que indica cuántas partes del entero o del grupo se consideran

$\frac{3}{4}$ ———numerator

Possible summaries:
My Vocabulary Summary

obtuse angle [äb•too′s ang′gəl] An angle that measures greater than 90° and less than 180°

ángulo obtuso Un ángulo que mide más de 90° y menos de 180°

obtuse triangle [äb•too′s trī′ang•gəl] A triangle with one obtuse angle

triángulo obtusángulo Un triángulo con un ángulo obtuso

order of operations [ôr′dər əv äp•ə•rā′shənz] A special set of rules which gives the order in which calculations are done

From left to right, multiply or divide, then add or subtract.

orden de las operaciones Un conjunto especial de reglas que establece el orden en que se hacen los cálculos

ounce (oz) [ouns] A customary unit for measuring weight;
1 pound = 16 ounces

A pencil weighs about 1 ounce.

onza (oz) Una unidad del sistema usual con la que se mide el peso;
1 libra = 16 onzas

An apple weighs about 5 ounces.

P

parallel lines [pâr′ə•lel līnz] Lines in the same plane that never intersect and are always the same distance apart

líneas paralelas Líneas ubicadas en un mismo plano que nunca se intersecan y siempre están a la misma distancia entre sí

Interactive Glossary

Possible summaries:
My Vocabulary Summary

parallelogram [pär•ə•lel'ə•gram]
A quadrilateral whose opposite sides are parallel and of equal length

paralelogramo Un cuadrilátero con lados opuestos paralelos y de igual longitud

partial product [pär'shəl prŏd'əkt]
A method of multiplying in which the ones, tens, hundreds, and so on are multiplied separately and then the products are added together

producto parcial Un método de multiplicación en el que las unidades, decenas, centenas, etc., se multiplican por separado y luego se suman los productos

$$36$$
$$\times 21$$

partial products
$$600 \leftarrow 20 \times 3 \text{ tens} = 60 \text{ tens}$$
$$120 \leftarrow 20 \times 6 \text{ ones} = 120 \text{ ones}$$
$$30 \leftarrow 1 \times 3 \text{ tens} = 3 \text{ tens}$$
$$+\ 6 \leftarrow 1 \times 6 \text{ ones} = 6 \text{ ones}$$
$$756$$

partial quotient [pär'shəl kwō'shənt]
A method of dividing in which multiples of the divisor are subtracted from the dividend and then the quotients are added together

cociente parcial Un método de división en el que los múltiplos del divisor se restan del dividendo y luego se suman los cocientes

$$228 \div 4 =$$
$$228 = 200 + 20 + 8$$
$$200 \div 4 = 50$$
$$20 \div 4 = 5$$ partial quotients
$$8 \div 4 = 2$$
$$50 + 5 + 2 = 57$$
$$228 \div 4 = 57$$

pattern [păt'ərn] An ordered set of numbers or objects; the order helps you predict what will come next

patrón Un conjunto ordenado de números u objetos; el orden permite predecir qué sigue a continuación.

2, 4, 6, 8, 10

♥ ♥ ☆ ♥ ☆
☆ ♥ ☆ ♥

perimeter [pə•rim'ə•tər] The distance around a figure

perímetro La distancia alrededor de una figura

$$P = 2 \times l + 2 \times w$$

J50 Glossary

Interactive Glossary

Possible summaries:
My Vocabulary Summary

period [pîr'ē•əd] Each group of three digits in a multi-digit number; periods are usually separated by commas or spaces.

período Cada grupo de tres dígitos en un número de varios dígitos; por lo general, los períodos suelen separarse con comas o espacios.

85,643,900 has three periods.

perpendicular lines [pər•pən•dik'yōō•lər līnz] Two lines that intersect to form four right angles

líneas perpendiculares Dos líneas que se intersecan y forman cuatro ángulos rectos

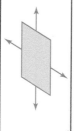

pint (pt) [pīnt] A customary unit for measuring capacity and liquid volume;
1 pint = 2 cups

pinta (pt) Una unidad del sistema usual con la que se mide la capacidad y el volumen líquido;
1 pinta = 2 tazas

A water bottle holds about 1 pint of water.

place value [plās val'yōō] The value of a digit in a number, based on the location of the digit

valor posicional El valor que tiene un dígito en un número según su ubicación

THOUSANDS			ONES		
Hundreds	Tens	Ones	Hundreds	Tens	Ones
1	3	6,	0	8	0

plane [plān] A flat surface that extends without end in all directions

plano Una superficie plana que se extiende sin fin en todas direcciones

point [point] An exact location in space

punto Una ubicación exacta en el espacio

• A

Glossary J51

Interactive Glossary

Possible summaries:
My Vocabulary Summary

pound (lb) [pound] A customary unit for measuring weight; 1 pound = 16 ounces

libra (lb) Una unidad del sistema usual con la que se mide el peso; 1 libra = 16 onzas

A soccer ball weighs about 1 pound.

prime number [prīm num'bər] A number that has exactly two factors: 1 and itself

número primo Un número que tiene exactamente dos factores: 1 y él mismo

2, 3, 5, 7, 11, 13, 17, and 19 are prime numbers.

product [prŏd'əkt] The answer to a multiplication problem

producto El resultado de una multiplicación

$7 \times 8 = 56$

factors   product

protractor [prō'trak•tər] A tool for measuring the size of an angle

transportador Un instrumento con el que se mide el tamaño de un ángulo

I can use a protractor to find the degree measure of an angle.

Interactive Glossary

Possible summaries:
My Vocabulary Summary

Q

quart (qt) [kwôrt] A customary unit for measuring capacity and liquid volume; 1 quart = 2 pints

cuarto (ct) Una unidad del sistema usual con la que se mide la capacidad y el volumen líquido; 1 cuarto = 2 pintas

A flower pot holds about 1 quart of soil.

quotient [kwō'shənt] The number that results from dividing

cociente Número que resulta de una división

$$12 \div 3 = 4 \quad \overset{4}{\underset{}{3\overline{)12}}} \longleftarrow \text{quotient}$$

quotient

R

ray [rā] A part of a line; it has one endpoint and continues without end in one direction.

semirrecta Una parte de una recta; tiene un extremo y continúa sin fin en una sola dirección.

$K \quad L$

rectangle [rek'tang•gəl] A quadrilateral with two pairs of parallel sides, two pairs of sides of equal length, and four right angles

rectángulo Un cuadrilátero con dos pares de lados paralelos de igual longitud y cuatro ángulos rectos

Interactive Glossary

Possible summaries:
My Vocabulary Summary

reflex angle [re′fleks′ ang′gəl] An angle that measures greater than 180° and less than 360°

ángulo de reflexión Ángulo cuya medida es mayor que 180° y menor que 360°

regroup [rē•grōōp′] To exchange amounts of equal value to rename a number

reagrupar Intercambiar cantidades de igual valor para convertir un número

5 ones + 8 ones = 13 ones or
1 ten 3 ones

regular polygon [reg′yə•lər pŏl′i•gŏn] A polygon that has all sides that are equal in length and all angles equal in measure

polígono regular Un polígono en el que todos los lados tienen la misma longitud y todos los ángulos tienen la misma medida

remainder [ri•mān′dər] The amount left over when a number cannot be divided equally

residuo La cantidad que queda cuando no se puede dividir un número en partes iguales

14 ÷ 3 is 4 r2

remainder

rhombus [rŏm′bəs] A quadrilateral with two pairs of parallel sides and four sides of equal length

rombo Un cuadrilátero con dos pares de lados paralelos y cuatro lados de igual longitud

right angle [rīt ang′gəl] An angle that forms a square corner

ángulo recto Un ángulo que forma una esquina cuadrada

Interactive Glossary

Possible summaries:
My Vocabulary Summary

right triangle [rīt trī′ang•gəl] A triangle with one right angle

triángulo rectángulo Un triángulo con un ángulo recto

round [round] To replace a number with another number that tells about how many or how much

redondear Reemplazar un número con otro número que indica una cantidad aproximada

35,368 rounded to the nearest ten thousand is 40,000.

S

scale [skāl] Numbers or marks arranged at regular intervals that are used for measurement or to establish position

escala Números o marcas dispuestos a intervalos regulares que se emplean para medir o establecer una posición

The scale on a protractor shows the measure of an angle.

scalene triangle [skā′lēn trī′ang•gəl] A triangle with no sides of equal length

triángulo escaleno Triángulo cuyos lados no son de la misma longitud

30 cm
13 cm
18 cm

Possible summaries:
My Vocabulary Summary

second (sec) [sĕk′ənd] A small unit of time;
1 minute = 60 seconds

segundo (s) Una unidad de tiempo pequeña;
1 minuto = 60 segundos

I can snap my fingers once in 1 second.

square [skwâr] A quadrilateral with two pairs of parallel sides, four sides of equal length, and four right angles

cuadrado Un cuadrilátero con dos pares de lados paralelos, cuatro lados de igual longitud y cuatro ángulos rectos

square unit [skwâr yōō′nĭt] A unit of area with dimensions of 1 unit × 1 unit

unidad cuadrada Una unidad de área con dimensiones de 1 unidad × 1 unidad

1 square unit

standard form [stăn′dərd fôrm] A way to write numbers by using the digits 0–9, with each digit having a place value

forma normal Una manera de escribir números usando los dígitos 0 a 9, en laque cada dígito ocupa un valor posicional

53,212

straight angle [strāt ăng′gəl] An angle that measures 180°

ángulo llano Ángulo que mide 180°

Possible summaries:
My Vocabulary Summary

T

tenth [tĕnth] One of ten equal parts

décimo Una de diez partes iguales

tenth

Written as a fraction:
$\frac{1}{10}$

Written as a decimal:
0.1

term [fûrm] A number or object in a pattern

término Un número u objeto en un patrón

2, 4, 6, 8, 10, 12

The numbers 2, 4, 6, 8, 10, and 12 are terms in this pattern.

ton (T) [fun] A customary unit used to measure weight;
1 ton = 2,000 pounds

tonelada (t) Una unidad del sistema usual que se usa para medir el peso;
1 tonelada = 2,000 libras

A small car weighs about 1 ton.

trapezoid [trap′i•zoid] *exclusive* A quadrilateral with exactly one pair of parallel sides

trapecio *exclusivo* Cuadrilátero con exactamente un par de lados paralelos

trapezoid [trap′i•zoid] *inclusive* A quadrilateral with at least one pair of parallel sides

trapecio *inclusivo* Cuadrilátero con al menos un par de lados paralelos

Interactive Glossary

Possible summaries:
My Vocabulary Summary

word form [wûrd fôrm] A way to write numbers by using words

en palabras Manera de escribir los números usando palabras

two thousand four hundred one

Y

yard (yd) [yärd] A customary unit for measuring length or distance; 1 yard = 3 feet

yarda (yd) Una unidad del sistema usual con la que se mide la longitud o la distancia; 1 yarda = 3 pies

The width of a desk is about 1 yard.

The height of a door is about 2 yards.

Interactive Glossary

Possible summaries:
My Vocabulary Summary

U

unit fraction [yoo'nit frak'shan] A fraction that has a numerator of one

fracción unitaria Una fracción que tiene un numerador de uno

$\frac{1}{3}$ $\frac{1}{8}$ $\frac{1}{10}$

V

vertex [vûr'teks] The point at which two rays of an angle meet or two (or more) line segments meet in a two-dimensional figure

vértice El punto en el que se unen dos semirrectas de un ángulo o dos (o más) segmentos de una figura bidimensional

vertex

W

weight [wāt] How heavy an object is

peso Cuán pesado es un objeto

Measure customary weight in ounces, pounds, and tons.

whole [hōl] All of the parts of a figure or group

entero Todas las partes de una figura o de un grupo

whole

Notes & Reflections

Index

D

data checkpoint, every module includes an autoscored Are You Ready? diagnostic assessment and a Module Test summative assessment. Every lesson includes an autoscored Check Understanding formative assessment. When you assign autoscored assignments on Ed: Your Friend in Learning, you will have immediate access to data and recommendations for differentiation.

Are You Ready?, appears in every module. 4, 30, 52, 76, 100, 132, 160, 184, 218, 240, 266, 297, 326, 362, 390, 420, 444, 468, 488, 514, 534

Check Understanding, appears in every lesson. *See, for example,* 8, 13, 17, 21, 25, 33, 37, 41, 44, 55, 59, 62, 66, 70, 79, 83, 87, 91, 94, 103

Module Test, *28A, 48A, 74A, 98A, 130A, 158A, 180A, 216A, 236A, 264A, 296A, 324A, 358A, 388A, 418A, 440A, 466A, 484A, 512A, 532A, 552A*

data-driven instruction, every module includes data charts to help you drive instruction to support students for the Are You Ready? and Module Review assessments. Every lesson includes differentiation support following Check Understanding assessment to support students. *Teacher Edition: Planning and Pacing Guide* PG24–PG31

data, on line plots, 507–510

decimal point, 300

decimals
compare, 311–314
defined, 300
as fractions, 299–302, 303–306, 307–310
money and, 315–318

decimeters (dm), 516, 520

degrees, 340

developing math language, *3C, 29C, 51C, 75C, 99C, 131C, 159C, 183C, 217C, 239C, 265C, 297C, 325C, 361C, 389C, 419C, 443C, 467C, 487C, 513C, 533C*

diagnostic assessment
Are You Ready? (*see* Are You Ready?)

difference, 35–38. *See also* subtraction

differentiated instruction, every lesson includes leveled activities for pulled small groups and leveled print and digital activities for Math Centers. Some examples are *5C, 11C, 15C, 19C, 23C, 31C, 35C, 39C, 43C, 53C, 57C, 61C, 65C, 69C, 77C, 81C, 85C, 89C, 93C, 101C*

digit, value of, 5–10. *See also* place value

distance, 493–496, 519–522

Distributive Property, 105–108, 110–111, 145–148, 197

divisibility rules, 248, 256

divisible, 248

division
check quotients, 171–174
Distributive Property and, 145–148
estimate quotients, 89–92

inverse operation of, 61–64
mental math strategies, 93–96
multistep problems with, 69–72, 175–178
partial quotients for, 153–156
patterns, 81–84
by place value, 165–170, 171–174
with regrouping, 161–164, 166–167
remainders, 137–140, 141–144
as repeated subtraction, 149–152
represent, 133–138, 161–164

dollars, 315–318, 319–322

doubling, 96, 187

E

elapsed time, 539–542, 543–546

endpoints, 328, 332

equations
for multistep problems, 125–128
for renaming fractions and mixed numbers, 395–398

equilateral triangle, 453–456, 473–478

equivalent decimals, 307–310

equivalent fractions
common multiples and, 283–286, 287–290, 291–294
as decimals, 307–310
generate, 279–282
models of, 275–279

estimate
defined, 24, 32
differences, 36–38
products, 85–88, 189–194, 207–210
quotients, 89–92
sums, 32–34

Exit Ticket, every lesson provides a projectable Exit Ticket. Some examples are *10, 14, 18, 22, 26, 34, 38, 42, 46, 56, 60, 64, 68, 72, 80, 84, 88, 92, 96, 104*

expanded form, 13–14, 109–112

F

factor pair, 242–243

factors. *See also* multiplication
defined, 247
number theory on, 241–244, 245–250, 251–254
of prime and composite numbers, 255–258

feet (ft), 489–492, 493–498

fluid ounces (fl oz), 503–506

formative assessment
Check Understanding (*see* Check Understanding)

formula
area, 219–222
defined, 43
perimeter of rectangle, 43–46

fractions
add
with common denominators, 361–366, 367–370, 371–374, 391–394
mixed numbers, 391–394, 399–404, 409–412, 413–416
with unlike denominators, 383–386
circle, fractional parts of, 335–338, 339–344 (*see also* manipulatives and materials)
compare, 267–270, 271–274, 287–290, 291–294
as decimals, 299–302, 303–306, 307–310
equivalent, 275–278, 279–282, 283–286, 291–294, 307–310
money and, 315–318
multiply, 421–424, 425–428, 429–434, 435–438
order, 291–294
rename, 395–398
subtract, 375–378, 379–382, 391–394, 413–416

fractions greater than one. *See* mixed numbers

front-end estimation, 191–192

G

gallons (gal), 490, 503–506

geometric pattern, 479–482

geometry
angles
draw and identify, 327–330, 345–348, 461–464
as fractional parts of a circle, 335–338, 339–340
join and separate, 349–352
measures of, 331–334, 345–348, 461–464
types of, 341–344, 449–452
unknown measures of, 353–356
lines and line segments
draw and identify, 327–330
types of, 445–448
rays, 327–330
shape patterns, 479–482
symmetry, lines of, 469–472, 473–478
two-dimensional figures
angles of, 449–452, 457–460, 461–464
lines of symmetry for, 473–478
quadrilateral, 457–460
shape patterns, 479–482
sides of, 453–456, 457–460
triangle, 449–452, 453–456

Glossary. *See More Practice and Homework Journal* for the student Interactive Glossary. See Teacher Edition: Planning and Pacing Guide PG116–PG128 for the teacher Interactive Glossary.

grams (g), 517

grouping. *See* Associative Property of Multiplication

Index

measurement
  angles
    draw and identify, 327–330, 345–348, 461–464
    as fractional parts of a circle, 335–338, 339–344
    measures of, 331–334, 345–348, 461–464
    types of, 341–344, 449–452
    unknown measures of, 353–356
  area (A)
    of combined shapes, 223–226
    defined, 220
    formula, 219–222
    problem solving with, 231–234
    of rectangle, 219–222, 223–226, 231–234
    unknown measures and, 227–230
  customary measurement units
    benchmarks for, 489–492
    for length, 493–498
    for liquid volume, 503–506
    problem solving with, 527–530
    for weight, 499–502
  metric measurement units
    benchmarks for, 515–518
    for length, 519–522
    for liquid volume, 523–526
    for mass, 523–526
    problem solving with, 527–530
  perimeter of rectangle, 43–46
meters (m), 516, 519–522
metric measurement units
  benchmarks for, 515–518
  for length, 519–522
  for liquid volume, 523–526
  for mass, 523–526
  problem solving with, 527–530
miles (mi), 490
milliliters (mL), 517, 525
millimeters (mm), 516, 519–522
minutes, 535–538, 539–542, 543–546
mixed numbers
  add, 391–394, 399–404, 409–412, 413–416
  defined, 396
  multiply, 435–438
  rename, 395–398, 405–408
  subtract, 391–394, 399–404, 405–408, 413–416
Module Opening Task, 3, 29, 51, 75, 99, 131, 159, 183, 217, 239, 265, 297, 325, 361, 389, 419, 443, 467, 487, 513, 533
module planning, *3A, 29A, 51A, 75A, 99A, 131A, 159A, 183A, 217A, 239A, 265A, 297A, 325A, 361A, 389A, 419A, 443A, 467A, 487A, 513A, 533A*
Module Review, every module includes a Module Review with a possible scoring guide for all items. *27–28, 47–48, 73–74, 97–98, 129–130, 157–158, 179–180, 215–216, 235–236, 263–264, 295–296, 323–324, 357–358, 387–388, 417–418, 439–440, 465–466, 483–484, 511–512, 531–532, 551–552*

Module Test, every module includes a Module Test with an alternate version. *28A, 48A, 74A, 98A, 130A, 158A, 180A, 216A, 236A, 264A, 296A, 324A, 358A, 388A, 418A, 440A, 466A, 484A, 512A, 532A, 552A*
money, 315–318, 319–322
multi-digit numbers. *See* whole numbers
multiples
  common, 283–286, 287–290
  of fractions, 421–424, 425–428
  generate using factors, 251–254
  multiply by, 185–188, 207–210
multiplication
  with area models, 105–108, 113–116, 195–198
  estimate products, 85–88, 189–194, 207–210
  expanded form for, 109–112
  of fractions, 421–424, 425–428, 429–434, 435–438
  inverse operation of, 61–64
  mental math strategies, 93–96
  of mixed numbers, 435–438
  by multiples of ten, 185–188, 207–210
  multistep problems with, 69–72, 175–178
  with partial products, 113–116, 195–198, 199–202, 207–210
  patterns, 77–80
  by place value, 117–120, 121–124, 207–210
  properties of, 93, 94, 105–108, 145–148, 187
  regroup for, 117–120, 121–124, 203–206
  represent, 101–104
multiplicative comparison problems, 53–56, 57–60, 61–64
multistep problems
  divide to solve, 69–72, 175–178
  equations for, 125–128
  with money, 319–322
  multiply to solve, 69–72, 175–178
  reasonableness of answers, 128, 176, 211–214

N

number patterns, 259–262
numbers
  compare
    decimals, 311–314
    fractions, 267–270, 271–274, 287–290, 291–294
    whole numbers, 19–22
  compatible numbers, 89–92, 192
  composite numbers, 255–258
  decimals
    compare, 311–314
    defined, 300
    as fractions, 299–302, 303–306, 307–310
    money and, 315–318
  fractions (*see* fractions)
  mixed numbers
    add, 391–394, 399–404, 409–412, 413–416
    defined, 396

  multiply, 435–438
  rename, 395–398, 405–408
  subtract, 391–394, 399–404, 405–408, 413–416
  place value of
    compare and order by, 19–22
    of decimals, 299–302, 303–306, 311–314
    defined, 5–7
    to divide, 165–170, 171–174
    to multiply, 117, 121–124, 185–188
    product patterns and, 77–80
    quotient patterns and, 81–84
    regroup by, 15–18 (*see also* regroup)
    relationships, 11–14
    rounding and, 23–26 (*see also* rounding)
  prime numbers, 255–258
  whole numbers (*see* whole numbers)
number theory
  composite numbers, 255–258
  factors, 241–244, 245–250, 251–254
  multiples, 251–254
  number patterns, 259–262
  prime numbers, 255–258

O

obtuse angles, 341
obtuse triangle, 449–452
octagon, 473–478
operations
  addition
    of angles, 349–352, 353–356
    of columns, 30
    estimate sums, 32–34
    of fractions with common denominators, 363–366, 367–370, 371–374, 391–394
    of fractions with unlike denominators, 383–386
    of mixed numbers, 391–394, 399–404, 409–412, 413–416
    properties of, 409–412
    of whole numbers, 31–34, 39–42
  division
    check quotients, 171–174
    Distributive Property and, 145–148
    estimate quotients, 89–92
    inverse operation of, 61–64
    mental math strategies, 93–96
    multistep problems with, 69–72, 175–178
    partial quotients for, 153–156
    patterns, 81–84
    by place value, 165–170, 171–174
    with regrouping, 161–164, 165–168
    remainders, 137–140, 141–144
    as repeated subtraction, 149–152
    represent, 133–136, 161–164

Index

operations *(continued)*

multiplication

with area models, 105–108, 113–116, 195–198

estimate products, 85–88, 189–194, 207–210

expanded form for, 109–112

of fractions, 421–424, 425–428, 429–434, 435–438

inverse operation of, 61–64

mental math strategies, 93–96

of mixed numbers, 435–438

by multiples of ten, 185–188, 207–210

multistep problems with, 69–72, 175–178

with partial products, 113–116, 195–198, 199–202, 207–210

patterns, 77–80

by place value, 117–120, 121–124, 207–210

properties of, 93, 94, 105–108, 145–148, 187

regroup for, 117–120, 121–124, 203–206

represent, 101–104

subtraction

of angles, 349–352, 353–356

division as repeated subtraction, 149–152

estimate differences, 35–38

of fractions, 375–378, 379–382, 391–394, 413–416

of mixed numbers, 391–394, 399–404, 405–408, 413–416

of whole numbers, 35–38, 39–42

order

data, on line plots, 507–510

fractions, 291–294

by place value, 19–22

property of (*see* Commutative Property of Addition; Commutative Property of Multiplication)

order of operations, 127

ounces (oz), 491–492, 499–502

P

pacing, *Teacher Edition: Planning and Pacing Guide* PG46–PG58

parallel lines, 445–448, 457–460

parallelogram, 457–460

partial products, 109–112, 113–116, 195–198, 199–202, 207–210

partial quotients, 153–156

patterns

defined, 259

number, 259–262

of products, 77–80

of quotients, 81–84

shape, 479–482

perimeter of rectangle, 43–46

period, in a multi-digit number, 7

perpendicular lines, 445–448, 457–460

pints (pt), 490, 503–506

place value

compare and order by, 19–22

of decimals, 299–302, 303–306, 311–314

defined, 5–7

to divide, 165–170, 171–174

to multiply, 117–120, 121–124, 211–214

product patterns and, 77–80

quotient patterns and, 81–84

regroup by, 15–18 (*see also* regroup)

relationships, 5–10, 11–14

rounding and, 23–26 (*see also* rounding)

points, 327–330

polygon, 449–452, 457–460, 473–478

pounds (lb), 491–492, 499–502

prerequisite skills. *See also* Are You Ready?

for addition, 30

for angles, 326

for area, 218

for decimals, 298

for division, 132, 160

for estimation, 76

for fractions, 266, 298, 362, 390, 420

for lines of symmetry, 468

for measurement, 488, 514

for multiplication, 100, 184

for number theory, 240

for patterns, 468

for place value, 4

for problem situations, 52

for subtraction, 30

for time, 534

for two-dimensional figures, 444

Prerequisite Skills Activity. *See under* Warm-Up Options

prime numbers, 255–258

Problem of the Day. *See under* Warm-Up options

problem solving

comparison problems (*see* comparison problems)

multistep problems (*see* multistep problems)

Problem Types, PG68–PG77

products. *See also* multiplication

estimate, 85–88, 189–194, 207–210

partial, 109–112, 113–116, 195–198, 199–202, 207–210

Professional Learning

About the Math, some examples are *61A, 89A, 113A, 121A, 141A, 165A, 189A, 207A, 223A, 251A*

Using Mathematical Practices and Processes, some examples are *15A, 35A, 65A, 85A, 101A, 109A, 117A, 149A, 153A*

Visualizing the Math, some examples are *39A, 57A, 93A, 105A, 145A, 175A, 195A, 231A, 241A, 287A*

properties of operations

Associative Property of Addition, 409–412

Associative Property of Multiplication, 94, 187

Commutative Property of Addition, 409–412

Commutative Property of Multiplication, 93

Distributive Property, 105–108, 110–111, 145–148, 197

Put It in Writing. *See* journal

Q

quadrilateral, 457–460

quarts (qt), 490, 503–506

quotients. *See also* division

check, 171–174

defined, 247

estimate, 89–92

partial, 153–156

place value in, 165–170

R

rays, 327–330

reasonableness of answers

of differences, 35–38

of multistep problems, 128, 176, 211–214

of products, 85–88, 114, 115, 118, 120, 203–205, 207, 208

of quotients, 89–92, 172

of sums, 31–34

rectangle

area of, 219–222, 223–226, 227–230, 231–234

attributes of, 457–460

perimeter formula for, 43–46, 227–230

reflex angles, 341

regroup

defined, 16

to divide, 161–164, 166–167

to multiply, 117–120, 121–124, 203–206

to rename numbers, 15–18

to subtract, 35–38

regular octagon, 473–478

regular polygon, 474–476, 482

remainders, 137–140, 141–144, 172, 176

rename

fractions, 308–310, 315, 383–386, 395–398

mixed numbers, 402, 405–408, 436

whole numbers, 15–18, 83, 186–187

repeated subtraction, 149–152

represent

addition, 31–32

angles, 327–330, 335–336, 339, 345–346, 348

area, 219

comparison problems, 39–40, 53–56, 57–60, 61–64, 65–68

composite numbers, 255

customary measurement units, 490–491, 493–494, 496–497, 499–500, 502, 503–504

division

Distributive Property and, 145–148

with equal groups, 133–136

partial quotients, 153–154

patterns, 81–82

place value and, 165–167

regrouping, 161–164

remainders, 137–140, 141–142

as repeated subtraction, 149

equivalent fractions as decimals, 307–308

estimations, 85–87, 89, 189

factors, 241–244, 245–246, 249

fractions
  add, 367–370, 371–374
  compare, 267–270, 271–274, 288, 290, 293
  decompose, 363–366
  equivalent, 275–278, 281–282
  multiply, 422–424, 425–428, 429–431
  subtract, 375–378, 379–381
hundredths, 303–306
lines, 329–330, 445, 447–448
lines of symmetry, 469–472, 473–478
metric measurement units, 515–517, 519–520, 523–524
mixed number addition and subtraction, 391–392, 399–404, 405–406
money, 315–318, 319
multiplication
  Distributive Property and, 105–108
  with equal groups, 101–104
  expanded form for, 109–110
  by multiples of ten, 185–186
  with partial products, 113–114, 195–198, 199
  patterns, 77–78
  by place value, 117–119, 121–122
prime numbers, 255
renaming, 395–396, 398, 405–406
shape patterns, 479–480
subtraction, 35–36
tenths, 299–302
time, 535, 539–542
whole numbers, 5–7, 11–12, 15–17, 19, 21, 23–24

Response to Intervention/Multi-Tiered System of Support (RtI/MTSS), options can be found at point of use. Some examples are *4, 5C, 11C, 15C, 19C, 23C, 27–28, 30, 47–48, 57C, 73–74, 81C, 97–98, 99B, 105C, 129–130. See also Teacher Edition: Planning and Pacing Guide PG42*

rhombus, 457–460

right angles, 341, 344, 353, 356, 446–447, 449–450, 457–460, 464

right triangle, 449–452

rounding
  to add, 32–34
  defined, 24
  to divide, 89–92
  to multiply, 85–88, 126, 190–194
  place value and, 23–26
  to subtract, 36–38

S

scalene triangle, 453–456

seconds, 535–538, 539–542, 543–546

shape patterns, 479–482

Sharpen Skills. *See under* Warm-Up Options

Spark Your Learning. *See under* student samples

square, 222, 229–230, 233–234, 457–460, 474, 477

square unit, 219–222

standard form, 11–14

standards correlations, *Teacher Edition: Planning and Pacing Guide PG61–PG66*

STEM Task, 1, 14, 38, 49, 72, 96, 174, 181, 188, 233, 237, 261, 278, 302, 348, 359, 386, 416, 441, 448, 459, 476, 485, 498, 526, 530

Step It Out. *See under* student samples

straight angles, 341

Stronger and Clearer Each Time. *See under* language routines

student samples
  Spark Your Learning, *5D, 11D, 15D, 19D, 23D, 31D, 35D, 39D, 53D, 57D, 77D, 81D, 85D, 89D, 101D, 105D, 109D, 113D, 117D, 121D, 125D, 133D, 137D, 141D, 145D, 149D, 153D, 161D, 165D, 219D, 241D, 245D, 267D, 271D, 275D, 299D, 303D, 307D, 327D, 331D, 335D, 339D, 363D, 367D, 371D, 375D, 379D, 391D, 395D, 399D, 405D, 421D, 425D, 429D, 445D, 469D, 489D, 493D, 499D, 503D, 519D, 523D*
  Step It Out, *43D, 61D, 65D, 69D, 93D, 171D, 175D, 203D, 223D, 227D, 231D, 251D, 255D, 259D, 279D, 283D, 287D, 311D, 315D, 319D, 345D, 349D, 353D, 383D, 413D, 449D, 453D, 457D, 461D, 473D, 479D, 539D, 543D*

subtraction
  of angles, 350–352, 353–356
  division as repeated subtraction, 149–152
  estimate differences, 36–38
  of fractions, 375–378, 379–382, 391–394, 413–416
  of mixed numbers, 391–394, 401–404, 405–408, 414–416
  of whole numbers, 35–38, 39–42

summative assessment
  Module Review (*see* Module Review)
  Module Test (*see* Module Test)

sums, 31–34. *See also* addition

symmetry, lines of, 469–472, 473–478, 479

T

Table of Measures. *See More Practice and Homework Journal*

Tabletop Flipcharts Mini-Lesson, every lesson includes a Tabletop Flipchart Mini-Lesson for teachers to use with a small, pulled group of students who are almost there. Some examples are *5C, 11C, 15C, 19C, 23C, 31C, 35C, 39C, 43C, 53C, 57C, 61C, 65C, 69C, 77C, 81C, 85C, 89C, 93C, 101C*

tally table, 507, 509–510

Teacher to Teacher, *3B, 29B, 51B, 75B, 99B, 131B, 159B, 183B, 217B, 239B, 265B, 297B, 325B, 361B, 389B, 419B, 443B, 467B, 487B, 513B, 533B*

Teaching for Depth, *3B, 29B, 51B, 75B, 99B, 131B, 159B, 183B, 217B, 239B, 265B, 297B, 325B, 361B, 389B, 419B, 443B, 467B, 487B, 513B, 533B*

technology and digital resources. *See* Ed: Your Friend in Learning for interactive instruction, interactive practice, and videos

tens patterns, 77–80, 81–84

tenths, 299–303

term, of patterns, 259–262

thousands patterns, 77–80

Three Reads. *See under* language routines

time
  compare units of, 535–538, 547, 549–550
  elapsed, 534, 539–542, 543–547, 550
  end, 543–547
  start, 543–547

tons (T), 491–492, 499, 501–502

trapezoid, 457–460, 473–478

triangle, 449–452, 453–456, 461, 464, 473–474, 476, 479–482

two-dimensional figures
  angles of, 449–452, 457–460, 461–464
  area (*A*)
    of combined shapes, 223–226, 231–234
    defined, 220
    formula, 219–222
    problem solving with, 231–234
    of rectangle, 219–222, 223–226, 227–230, 231–234
    unknown measures and, 227–230
  lines of symmetry for, 473–478
  perimeter of, 43–46, 227–230
  quadrilateral, 457–460
  shape patterns, 479–482
  sides of, 453–456, 457–460
  triangle, 449–452, 453–456

U

unit fraction, 364–366, 421–424

Unit Performance Task, PG85–PG91

unit square, 219–222

unknowns
  angle measures, 357–358
  area measures, 231–234

unlike denominators, 287–290, 291–294, 383–386

Unpacking Math Standards, *5A, 11A, 31A, 35A, 43A, 53A, 57A, 61A, 69A, 77A, 81A, 101A, 105A, 133A, 161A, 175A, 185A, 189A, 211A, 219A, 241A, 245A, 255A, 259A, 271A, 275A, 279A, 299A, 307A, 311A, 327A, 331A, 335A, 339A, 349A, 363A, 367A, 371A, 383A, 391A, 395A, 399A, 421A, 445A, 449A, 469A, 479A, 489A, 493A, 499A, 503A, 507A, 515A, 527A, 535A, 539A*

Using Mathematical Practices and Processes. *See under* Professional Learning

Index